A Jewel in the Pacific Flyway

A JEWEL IN THE PACIFIC FLYWAY

The Story of
Gray Lodge Wildlife Area

JOHN B. COWAN

California
Waterfowl
Association

The publication of this book is made possible by a donation to
the California Waterfowl Association from the Trione Foundation.

Managing editor: Judith Dunham
Cover and interior design: Poulson Gluck Design
Maps: Charles Denson
Proofreaders: Linda Bouchard, Jonathan Kauffman
Indexer: Ken DellaPenta

California Waterfowl Association
4630 Northgate Boulevard, Suite 150
Sacramento, CA 95834
916-648-1406
Web site: www.calwaterfowl.org

Printed and bound in Singapore by Tien Wah Press

Library of Congress Control Number on file
ISBN 0-9713000-0-3

Contents

Foreword

The spectacle of waterfowl migration is a phenomenon that brings to every naturalist a deep feeling of admiration and a respect for the awesome beauty of nature. From the East Coast to the West Coast, waterfowl enthusiasts see the beginning of this annual parade as the first sign of autumn. We begin to anticipate the change of seasons and the beauty of the many species of waterfowl and other migrants as they fly to their winter habitats.

Presented here, with outstanding revelations about wildlife, is the autobiography of dedicated naturalist, photographer, and professional habitat manager John Cowan. Professionally trained and attuned through years of field experience, John gives us a full panorama of his association with wildlife at his "Jewel in the Pacific Flyway." Vividly portrayed with his accomplished photography and detailed descriptions, it is a primer for individuals beginning to realize the significance of wildlife and a must for those of us who have enjoyed this gift of nature these past many years.

During my past four decades of friendship with John, we have enjoyed many experiences, but one of my most vivid memories is from 1975, when we were invited by the Alaska Fish and Game Division to visit the nesting grounds of the tule goose. Until that time, the exact location of the nesting grounds was not known. Since Gray Lodge Wildlife Area typifies the Central Valley wintering habitat of the tule goose, we had more than a passing interest. The time we spent with the Alaskan staff, corralling and banding the flightless, molting geese, was a most pleasant and instructive experience.

In the twenty-first century, when we read of the past abundance of wildlife and correlate its inevitable decline with human activity, we must acknowledge those individuals and organizations that anticipated the need for compatible cohabitation between wildlife and man. Step by step, they structured wildlife management so that we are now assured of maintaining the ecological balance so essential for nature's preservation into the foreseeable future and hopefully into perpetuity, even with a diminished habitat base.

Our gratitude extends to individuals across the nation who saw the dangers of overzealous harvesting and habitat loss. We are grateful for the state and federal legislation that established systems for structuring and monitoring game harvest. These successful programs were put in place to provide wildlife habitat through government protection and private landowner incentive and education programs.

Hunter conservationists should also be acknowledged for establishing nonprofit organizations that address habitat concerns. These stewards of our wetlands and wildlife resources include the Delta Waterfowl Foundation, Ducks Unlimited, the National Audubon Society, the Nature Conservancy, and the California Waterfowl Association, as well as other similar alliances throughout the nation. In our own state, the progressive cooperation of the California Department of Fish and Game and the U.S. Fish and Wildlife Service plays a vital and influential role in the overall system.

Today, landowners are encouraged to leave portions of their farmlands idle, restore wetland areas, and create a mosaic of agricultural and natural habitat to accommodate wildlife. In this way, wildlife can benefit from both public and privately owned lands throughout the flyways of North America.

There are many areas that are "jewels" in the Pacific Flyway, from Canada to Mexico, and surely other flyways can boast of similar wealth. In John Cowan's memorable book, he funnels our concentration into his own vivid experiences and outstanding photographs of his personal jewel— the Gray Lodge.

— HENRY TRIONE
Santa Rosa, California

Introduction

I was truly blessed to have been able to spend almost all of my working years in a career I loved and strongly believed in: wildlife habitat development and management. My interest in wildlife started early. I grew up on a twenty-acre ranch in Carmichael, a suburb of Sacramento. My home was a mile or so from the American River. A wide band of natural habitat ran along the river, and that is where I spent almost all my free time, with my good friend Rusty Clark. I learned a lot about the diversity of wildlife to be found where there is water, space, and good vegetative food and cover. From the seventh grade on, I had the responsibility of a large family garden. I learned about soils, their attributes and limitations, and the importance of water.

After graduating from Sacramento Junior College in 1938, I began my career with what was then called the California Division of Fish and Game. The entry position was Assistant Fish and Game Warden I. As part of the excellent training program, trainees were rotated to various sites throughout the state about every three or four months to gain exposure and experience working on different projects before receiving a permanent assignment.

For me, every rotation was an interesting learning experience. I had a turn at checking sardine deliveries at a fish reduction plant in Richmond, assisted on a patrol boat out of Martinez, and planted fish on both sides of the Sierra Nevada as well as in the Middle and North Forks of the American River. I spent rotations at the Mt. Shasta, Mt. Whitney, and Lake Tahoe fish hatcheries and participated in a mackerel-tagging research project out of Long Beach and Catalina Island and another at the Chino Game Farm. But when I was assigned to Joice Island Refuge near Suisun, I soon knew that a marsh, with its great variety of wildlife and habitat, was where I ultimately wanted to work.

By the time the rotations were completed, I also knew I needed more education. I applied for and was granted educational leave from the Division of Fish and Game. I went to Chico State College for a degree in biology and worked summers for the division, primarily planting trout.

Just as I was finishing at Chico State, World War II broke out. I enlisted in the Naval Flight Training Program and became a fighter–dive bomber pilot.

After the war, I enrolled at the University of California, Berkeley, to work for a master's degree in zoology. It was my great fortune to have Dr. A. Starker Leopold as professor and master's thesis chairman. I gained a mentor and formed a friendship that lasted for his lifetime. While in Berkeley, I worked part-time at the Division of Fish and Game food habits laboratory in Strawberry Canyon.

After I finished the required classes at U.C. Berkeley, I returned to work full-time as Assistant Game Biologist I on the state's Pheasant Research Project. This was also a good learning experience. Project leader Howard Twinning was an outstanding wildlife researcher, and I was fortunate to spend sixteen months working under his guidance.

In the fall of 1947, I had an offer that determined my next thirty-two and a half years with the division. I was asked to become manager of Gray Lodge Refuge. I readily accepted. At last, a refuge, a marsh. This book traces the development of Gray Lodge from a 2,540-acre inviolate waterfowl sanctuary to an 8,400-acre wildlife area. The idea first espoused by Aldo Leopold—that humans could and should develop habitat specifically for the protection and enhancement of wildlife—was still relatively new when I started at Gray Lodge. There was little prior research or information for guidance. But having been given cow pastures to turn into a home for wildlife, I did my best. An informal program brought together the state's few refuge managers a few times each year. The exchange of ideas and the discussion of successes and failures were very helpful. I have fond memories of the kinship among these early pioneers in game management. As it became obvious that what we did to enhance game species also benefited other wildlife, our focus widened. We became wildlife managers instead of game managers. This book is about those years of growth, changes of focus, expansion of vision, and hard work as reflected through the development of one area, Gray Lodge Wildlife Area.

The accompanying photographs were taken during my years at Gray Lodge. I started taking photographs initially to document sightings and to augment the many reports required. As the habitat developments took hold, I wanted to document the increase in the variety of species that use and depend on marshlands. Some of the material and photographs in this book have been published previously, particularly in articles in the California Department of Fish and Game magazine, *Outdoor California.*

Humans have always been fascinated by the great diversity of wildlife around them. There is no yardstick to measure the aesthetic, cultural, and spiritual values of human contact with other living creatures. These intangible values are personal, touching each of us in individual ways. Wildlife has a permanent place in our culture and, by law, is "held in trust" by and for the public. That public trust demands good stewardship and a responsibility to future generations. A major part of that trust is fulfilled through the development and maintenance of our wildlife areas.

— John B. Cowan

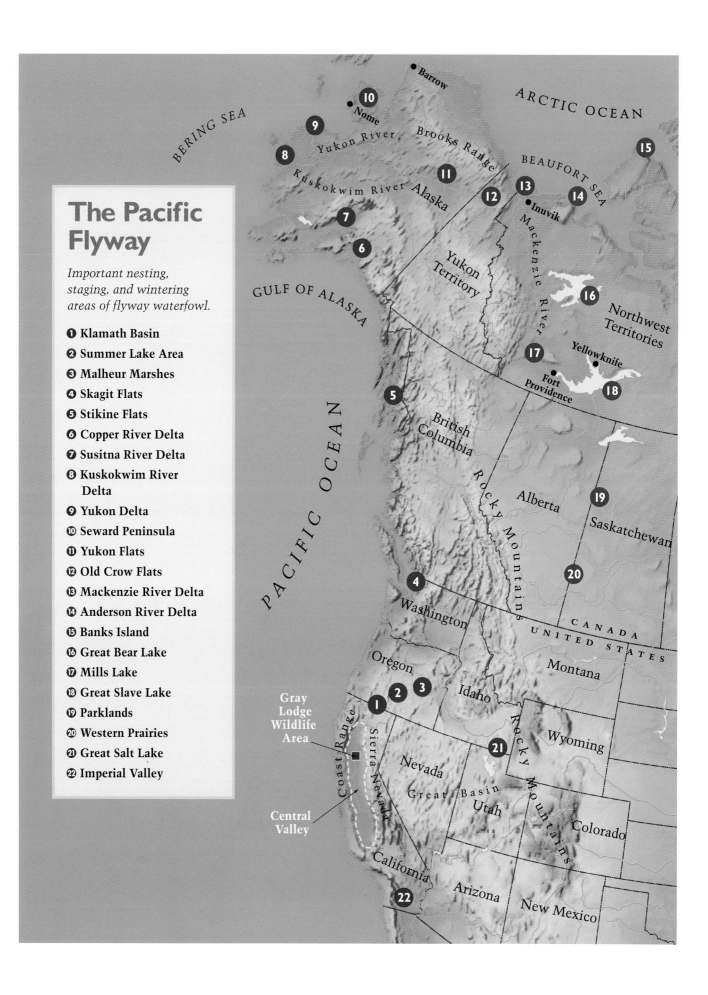

The Pacific Flyway

Important nesting, staging, and wintering areas of flyway waterfowl.

❶ Klamath Basin
❷ Summer Lake Area
❸ Malheur Marshes
❹ Skagit Flats
❺ Stikine Flats
❻ Copper River Delta
❼ Susitna River Delta
❽ Kuskokwim River Delta
❾ Yukon Delta
❿ Seward Peninsula
⓫ Yukon Flats
⓬ Old Crow Flats
⓭ Mackenzie River Delta
⓮ Anderson River Delta
⓯ Banks Island
⓰ Great Bear Lake
⓱ Mills Lake
⓲ Great Slave Lake
⓳ Parklands
⓴ Western Prairies
㉑ Great Salt Lake
㉒ Imperial Valley

Barrow
Nome
ARCTIC OCEAN
BERING SEA
Yukon River
Brooks Range
BEAUFORT SEA
Kuskokwim River
Alaska
Inuvik
Mackenzie River
Yukon Territory
GULF OF ALASKA
Northwest Territories
Yellowknife
Fort Providence
British Columbia
Rocky Mountains
Alberta
Saskatchewan
PACIFIC OCEAN
Washington
Oregon
Idaho
Montana
CANADA
UNITED STATES
Gray Lodge Wildlife Area
Coast Range
Sierra Nevada
Central Valley
Nevada
Great Basin
Utah
Wyoming
Colorado
California
Arizona
New Mexico

CHAPTER 1

Journeys Along the Pacific Flyway

The Pacific Flyway is one of four regions of North America identified nearly a century ago as biologists pieced together patterns of waterfowl migration across the continent. Flyways are based on geographic features rather than international borders. They incorporate a range of habitats from vast grasslands to forests, foothills to high deserts, and they are separated from one another along distinctive landscape features such as watersheds, forest edges, and mountain ranges. Flyways define a general regional division for wildlife management, but there is no hard-and-fast rule that individual birds migrate along one flyway to the exclusion of all others. Furthermore, flyway boundaries blend together, especially at their northern- and southernmost extensions. They are most distinct only in their central ranges. The Pacific Flyway extends from Alaska and northwestern Canada south into Mexico. It is bordered on the west by the Pacific Ocean. To the east, it includes much of western Canada and reaches the Rocky Mountains in the United States.

For waterfowl, seasonal travel along flyways is related to the transitional availability of food, water, and shelter—the basic requirements for survival. Along the Pacific Flyway, many waterfowl, shorebirds, and hawks, for instance, take advantage of seasonally

Flight of Ross's Geese
Ross's geese, along with snow geese, follow the Pacific Flyway and make up more than 50 percent of the total population of migrating geese in California. Heading south from northern Canada and Alaska, they usually fly at an elevation of three thousand feet. The birds follow the flyway's valleys and rivers, and do not hesitate to fly over mountain ranges to reach a destination.

abundant food supplies in northern parts of the flyway to fly in, nest, and raise their young while the weather is mild. As the weather turns harsh in autumn, these birds head south to areas where the competition for food and shelter is increased but where conditions are more tolerable. The Central Valley of California, where the Sacramento Valley and Gray Lodge Wildlife Area are located, is the principal wintering ground for Pacific Flyway waterfowl. While some waterfowl make extensive annual treks north and south, others within the flyway make no or very short migrations. For example, many mallards that winter in California's Central Valley nest there as well. Their travels occur in late spring and summer when they migrate to Oregon and Washington to molt, where wetlands are plentiful and disease risks are reduced. Still other waterfowl,

Coniferous Forest Marsh Habitat
(OPPOSITE)
The town of Yellowknife is located on the upper arm of the Great Slave Lake of the Northwest Territories of Canada. I hiked the area around the town and flew over it. The ponds provide a variety of food plants and escape cover for waterfowl.

Mt. Shasta (OPPOSITE)
Pacific Flyway waterfowl migrate south from a wide range of nesting areas. They stop to rest and feed at Tule Lake and other refuges in the Klamath Basin National Wildlife Refuge Complex on the Oregon-California border. A landmark for the travelers is majestic Mt. Shasta, about twenty-five miles from Tule Lake. As the birds head south, they typically fly along the east side of the great 14,162-foot mountain.

including some Canada geese and wood ducks, never migrate along the flyway, opting instead to reside year-round in habitats that provide all of their basic life requirements in a single, usually southern location.

My interest in the Pacific Flyway began when I came to Gray Lodge, which supported many thousands of migratory and resident species. I wanted to know more about migration, to see firsthand some of the nesting grounds of the birds that came to winter in the Sacramento Valley. Although nesting occurs in every region of the flyway, Alaska and the western prairies and parklands of Canada supply many of the waterfowl that winter in California. Fortunately, I had the opportunity to make three memorable journeys to those areas.

My first trip was to the Northwest Territories of Canada in July and August of 1972. I was one of a party of fifteen who traveled in cargo canoes eleven hundred miles down the great Mackenzie River from Fort Providence, on Great Slave Lake, north to the Arctic Ocean. My purpose was to see migration

Northern Pintail Courtship Flight (ABOVE)

Pintail drakes (left) begin courting females in late October and early November, hoping to be chosen as a mate before the return trip to the northern nesting grounds. By mid-January, about 85 percent of the ducks are paired up. Pintails have become known as the widest wanderers of all waterfowl. Ducks banded in California have been taken on the Cook Islands in the South Pacific; others have been recorded in several Siberian locations as well as Japan, some Central and South American areas, the Bahamas, and Hawaii. In 1996, a hen pintail banded in Japan showed up on the lower reaches of the Columbia River in Oregon only three months later.

Pintail Hen and Brood

Northern pintails nest all along the Pacific Flyway. The majority that winter in the Central Valley migrate north to breeding grounds in Canada and Alaska. Only six to eight pairs remain to nest on Gray Lodge, although significant numbers nest in California's San Joaquin Valley, Suisun Marsh, and northeastern high-desert marsh areas.

Mackenzie River Delta (LEFT)

This is only a small slice of the huge Mackenzie River Delta, which is about forty miles wide and a hundred miles long. The delta is a major staging area as well as nesting area. Snow geese that nest on Banks Island, about four hundred miles to the northeast, and along the arctic coast gather at the delta. From there, the birds journey to their wintering grounds, primarily the Central Valley of California and the highlands of Mexico.

Ponds of the Boreal Forest Region (RIGHT)

As is typical in Canada's Northwest Territories, particularly on the east side of the Mackenzie River, this pond has a stable water level and abundant aquatic plants that provide choice foods and excellent nesting cover for waterfowl.

Northern Shoveler (BOTTOM LEFT)

Some northern shovelers winter along the coastal areas of Washington and Oregon. Greater numbers are found along the California coast, and shovelers are also common in the Central Valley and Imperial Valley. Many shovelers, however, fly on to winter as far south as Guatemala.

Green-winged Teal (BOTTOM RIGHT)

This species of teal winters all along the Pacific Flyway, from British Columbia south through most of California and into southern Mexico.

routes as well as staging and nesting areas that I had read about. Before my canoe trip, I hired a bush pilot with a floatplane to fly me over the Mills Lake area about twenty miles downriver from Fort Providence.

It was easy to understand why Mills Lake is a major stopover point for waterfowl in both northern and southern migrations. Located on the east side of the Mackenzie, the lake provides approximately ten square miles of shallow wetlands for resting and staging and heavy stands of pondweeds, choice waterfowl food plants. Mills Lake is especially significant in the spring migration back to arctic breeding grounds as a place to stop while awaiting the ice breakup in the Mackenzie River Delta and vast stretches of arctic tundra. We had a good low-level flight over this area and landed for a short visit at a U.S.-Canadian wildlife services cooperative banding station on the lake. The pilot then landed in the middle of the Mackenzie River, where I joined the canoe party.

Long-distance Fliers
Snow geese fly farther north to nest than any other geese of the Pacific Flyway. The two major nesting areas are Banks Island, in the Canadian arctic, and Wrangel Island in Russia, several hundred miles off the north coast of Siberia. Only about 10 percent of North America's snow geese, but most Ross's geese, winter in California.

Ross's and Snow Geese
These geese come a long way to the heartland of their wintering area, the Sacramento Valley. The nesting grounds of Ross's geese were unknown until 1940, when a small colony was located in the Queen Maud Gulf Lowlands in Canada's Northwest Territories. At that time, the Ross's population was quite low. Since the late 1950s, Ross's geese have had the most successful prolonged increase in numbers of any of the Pacific Flyway geese.

A JEWEL IN THE PACIFIC FLYWAY

**Yukon-Kuskokwim
River Deltas**

*These two river deltas, only
twenty miles apart, make up
more than 20 million acres
of habitat for waterfowl,
shorebirds, and other wetland-
dependent wildlife. This view
shows one of the best breeding
areas of the entire Pacific
Flyway. The Central Valley
of California is one of the
major wintering areas for
birds hatched here. In 1978,
I spent time with U.S. Fish
and Wildlife Service biologist
Chris Dau, assisting in nesting
study surveys of the area.*

As the party progressed down the river, I
learned that very little waterfowl nesting occurs
right along the river itself, due to considerable
fluctuations in the water level in spring. Waterfowl nesting is primarily on the east side, starting
one hundred yards or so from the river's edge,
extending eastward where ancient icefields have
left thousands of ponds and lakes with fairly stable
water levels.

When we reached Inuvik, on the eastern edge
of the Mackenzie River Delta, I contacted Dr. Tom
Barry, a Canadian biologist in charge of waterfowl banding and research projects in the area of
the Mackenzie Delta, Arctic Ocean, and Beaufort
Sea. At his headquarters at the Anderson River
Research Station, Barry described the waterfowl
banding that had been done over the previous
twelve years at Banks Island and in the Anderson
and Mackenzie River Deltas. The results showed

Long-billed Curlew

*The range of this short-distance migrant in
the sandpiper family is confined to western
North America. Curlews nest from southern
Canada to central Nevada and Utah, and
from northeastern California to Wyoming
and Montana. In fall, some of the curlew
population migrates to the coastal and
inland marshes of California. Other birds
winter in Baja California and Mexico.*

Tundra Swans (LEFT AND BOTTOM)
When I flew over the Yukon River Delta at an elevation of about 500 feet, I could easily spot the many swans nesting in the brown tundra vegetation below. Traditionally, the majority of these swans followed the Pacific Flyway to winter in the Sacramento–San Joaquin Delta. Now that rice farmers flood their harvested fields in winter, many swans winter in the upper Sacramento Valley.

that birds from all four flyways nested in these areas. Of special interest to me were the reports that snow geese nesting on Banks Island in the Northwest Territories joined other snow geese from smaller colonies in the deltas to fly down the Pacific Flyway to Central California's wintering grounds. Barry asked his pilot to give me an extensive aerial tour of the area on the return trip to Inuvik. This flight over the Kugalak and Anderson River Deltas, over the Mackenzie River Delta, and along the coastal barren grounds was the highlight of the trip for me. It pleased me to see that there were still such good waterfowl nesting grounds on the North American continent.

On my second trip, in June and July of 1973, I went to Alaska and the headquarters of what was then the Clarence Rhodes National Wildlife Refuge and is now the Yukon Delta National Wildlife Refuge. Refuge manager Dr. Cal Lensink flew me by floatplane to a research cabin just a few miles from the coast and then left me there for a week. It was exhilarating to hike the spongy tundra each day and observe the abundance of nesting

A JEWEL IN THE PACIFIC FLYWAY

birds. The western Yukon Delta refuge contains more than 15 million acres of choice wetland and upland nesting habitat. Nesting in the delta generally does not begin until late May. Thus, young broods are not hatched out until the end of June, when ponds have thawed, aquatic insects are at the peak of abundance, and marsh plants are most nutritious.

For two of the days, I explored the area with biologist Chris Dau, who was conducting nesting studies at a research station three miles away. I saw how the seventy-five thousand lakes and ponds, the vast tidal flats,

Susitna River Delta (RIGHT)
The coastal flats of the Susitna River Delta, about thirty-five miles south of Anchorage, support a high number of nesting greater white-fronted geese. In 1981, my friend Henry Trione and I flew to Anchorage and met with Dan Timm, Alaska's State Waterfowl Studies coordinator. We assisted him and his crew in the banding of geese on the Susitna Flats.

Greater White-fronted Geese (LEFT)
Taking off from staging areas in the Yukon River Delta, white-fronted geese, seen in the foreground, fly nonstop down to Summer Lake in Oregon or the Tule-Klamath Lakes in Northern California, a distance of about twenty-three hundred miles. With an average speed of forty-five miles per hour, that makes about fifty-one hours of continuous flight time—one of the longest nonstop flights of any geese. After their long journey, the birds may spend a week or two in the Klamath Basin area, then make an overnight flight to the Sacramento Valley wintering grounds.

and the tundra hummocks of lichens, mosses, and dwarf arctic shrubs combined to provide nesting habitat for many species of waterfowl as well as shorebirds, terns, loons, and many other birds that migrate down the Pacific Flyway.

Five years later, in late June, I returned to Alaska, this time with my good friend Lee Otterson of Colusa, flying there in his twin-engine Aerostar. The two of us went by floatplane to the same research cabin at the peak of the nesting season. While hiking the area with Chris Dau, we observed tundra swans, greater white-fronted geese, cackling Canada geese, black brant, lesser sandhill cranes, and emperor geese, all with broods—and all, except the emperor geese, regular winter migrants to California. In the tundra, broods were watched constantly by their parents, as predators were continually searching for unprotected young. On two separate days, we saw goslings that lagged behind taken in the blink of an eye, one by a glaucous gull, the other by a jaeger.

When we left the area, we flew north to the Yukon River and followed it for over one thousand miles to the several fingers that reach out into the Bering Sea. We then flew over key Alaskan nesting grounds and migration routes—at an elevation generally flown by migrating waterfowl. From the Yukon River Delta, we followed the Alaska coastline around the Norton Sound to Nome, then headed around the coast and bays of the Seward Peninsula. Continuing north along the coast, we reached Barrow and headed over the Brooks Range to interior Alaska's Yukon Flats, where nearly one million ducks

Western Grebe

Most western grebes that winter in California nest primarily in the Tule and Klamath Lakes in the Klamath Basin, where this photograph was taken. Grebes like large lakes with marshy edges for nesting. In the fall, these grebes migrate to lakes, reservoirs, and coastal areas throughout the state.

A JEWEL IN THE PACIFIC FLYWAY

and geese are raised annually. Retracing our route home, we flew, as waterfowl do in migration, by way of the inland coastal passage areas of southeast Alaska to British Columbia and south toward Pacific Flyway wintering grounds in the Central Valley.

A real plus of those trips was the friendships developed with professionals who took me out and shared with me how they did their work and what they were learning. We should all be grateful to these Alaskan pilot-biologists whose aerial surveys and banding activities since the early 1950s have provided a foundation of knowledge of the Alaskan breeding grounds—a foundation that all who followed have built on. In fact, waterfowl biologists proliferated all along the Pacific Flyway, from Alaska to the Mexican border, as new state and federal waterfowl areas were established during the 1950s, 1960s, and 1970s. We were a loose fraternity, aware of one another's work through word of mouth as well as through professional conferences and journals. We visited other areas when possible and, in turn, were happy to show off our areas to colleagues.

I think back to November of 1947, when I first came to Gray Lodge. By that time, many of the wintering waterfowl had already arrived. Each day, I patrolled the refuge area, amazed and awestruck. The variety of birds, the numbers, the sounds were mind-boggling. But that first fall was nothing compared with all the years to come when I annually witnessed the entire sequence of arrival, winter movements, residence, and departure as the birds flew to their Pacific Flyway nesting grounds.

Avocet and Nestlings
American avocets on the Pacific Flyway nest in northeastern California, northern Nevada, southern Utah, and central Oregon and Washington. Some nests are just a scrape in the gravel or soil. Others, like this one, are built up with plant material. In the fall, a small number of migrating avocets stop at Gray Lodge Wildlife Area to feed and rest for a day or two on their way to winter in the marshes of coastal California. Others continue as far as southern Mexico and Central America.

CHAPTER 2

Sacramento Valley Wildlife History

Centuries ago, the Sacramento Valley provided one of the greatest havens for wildlife on the North American continent. In size, the valley is still impressive, extending 130 miles from Red Bluff on the north to the Sacramento–San Joaquin River Delta on the south, sandwiched between the Coast Ranges on the west and the Sierra Nevada foothills on the east. Try, for a moment, to picture this beautiful, bountiful region before the arrival of the first white men. Streams meandered to form oxbows, pools, and dead-end sloughs, all rich in sediment soils. Summer and autumn months brought shallow, quiet water. In winter and spring, rainstorms and rapid snowmelt sent great volumes of water and debris into the waterways. Riverbanks regularly overflowed. At high-water and flood stages, rivers spread throughout the sloughs, swales, oxbows, and low basins. Alkali flats and vernal pools were filled or covered entirely. Large areas of tule swamplands, called tularies, often formed on both sides of the inner valley streams.

Over the years, the rich soils along the streams produced riparian woodland belts, some over a mile wide. These thickets of native plants contained willow, cottonwood, sycamore, valley oak, and black walnut trees, often draped with wild grape. The ground was cloaked in elderberry, wild rose, and many other varieties of vegetation.

Historic Abundance
The Sacramento Valley was a wintering paradise for waterfowl before the settlement of the white man beginning in the early 1800s. Concentrations of geese (opposite) would have been a common sight to the native Maidu Indians. Numerous ducks, such as northern pintails (above), also nested in the valley.

Winter in the Sutter Buttes

To control winter flooding and conserve water, Shasta Dam was completed in the 1950s, followed by Oroville Dam in the 1960s. This photograph was taken January 2, 1984, when even the two dams could not hold the waters back. Imagine what the area must have been like for the native people and the wildlife in the previous century. In times of flood, the Indians and land animals found refuge in the buttes.

Wood ducks, abundant residents of the Sacramento Valley, nested in tree cavities. Beaver ponds, common along the streams, provided nesting habitat, as well as loafing and feeding areas, for waterfowl. Mallards, gadwalls, northern shovelers, cinnamon teal, northern pintails, redheads, and ruddy ducks surely nested here as they still do today. A healthy population of almost all marsh-associated birds filled the Great Valley, especially in winter. Nowhere would this abundance have been more evident than around the Sutter Buttes, in an area encompassing about thirty miles beyond their footholds, in the center of the northern Sacramento Valley. The buttes, approximately nine miles in diameter, are unique, rising abruptly from the valley floor into peaks reaching twenty-one hundred feet. Of volcanic origin, the buttes are often referred to as the world's smallest mountain range. Major waterways in the area are the Sacramento, Feather, and Yuba Rivers, along with Butte Creek, whose waters form a natural year-round wetland on the west side of the buttes.

John Bidwell was one of the early white explorers of the Sacramento Valley. His records give us a good picture of the valley when it still belonged to the native people. Regarding a trip on horseback up through

the area in March 1843, he wrote: "Hastening up the valley . . . the plains were dotted with scattering groves of spreading oak, while the clover and wild grasses, three and four feet high, were most luxuriant . . . and as I proceeded up the valley . . . I was struck with wonder and delight. . . . We were seldom or never out of sight of game, deer, elk, antelope and grizzly bears. Approaching Butte Creek, we camped. . . . Here we had an episode with grizzly bears which will afford some idea of that region in its natural state. In the spring . . . the bears lived chiefly on clover which grew luxuriantly. We first saw one, which made for the timber, two or three miles away; soon another, then more, all abounding away to the creek. At one time there were sixteen in the grove."

THE MAIDU INDIANS inhabited the area east of the Sacramento River and north of the Sutter Buttes, where their sizable communities thrived prior to the 1840s. John Work led a Hudson Bay Company Fur Brigade into the Sacramento Valley in the fall and winter of 1832–33. On January 2,

Northern Pintails

Pintails have always been the most numerous of the waterfowl that winter in California. They are the first waterfowl to arrive from northern nesting grounds; some are here as early as August. As natural habitat gave way to rice production in the Sacramento Valley, the birds readily adapted to feeding in rice fields.

1833, after a day spent traveling nine miles down the Feather River toward the buttes, he recorded in his journal: "The Indians were exceedingly numerous along the river. Our day's journey was short yet we passed six villages and are encamped near another, the inhabitants of each must amount to some hundreds. The country must be rich in resources when such numbers of people find subsistence." Several members of his company were Indians native to the eastern United States. Work's journal reports that they were amazed at what they saw, saying that in all their travels across the continent they had never seen an area with as much wildlife as in the Sacramento Valley.

Although tule elk, deer, antelope, and grizzly bears were in abundance, the Maidu did not kill large land animals in significant numbers. This explains why animal hides were used so little for housing, clothing, blankets, and other items, compared with the practices of other Native American groups. A single hunter might stalk deer with a deer-head mask and a bow and arrow. Group hunts were organized occasionally. On December 31, 1832, John Work recorded: "Raised camp and proceeded across the low ground to Feather River 12 miles E. . . . On reaching the river today, we met a party of near 200 Indians, several of them loaded with antelope meat. It appears that in company with the inhabitants of some villages below, they had been out hunting. Their mode is to surround the herd. Very few of the hunters seemed armed. Some had bows and arrows and a few of them short lances pointed with stone."

Today, we are impressed by the 3 to 4 million waterfowl that migrate to spend the winter in the Sacramento Valley. The winter waterfowl concentrations must have been mind-boggling when the valley was primarily one big wetland. The Maidu left no written records, but excerpts from early journals give us an inkling: "Waterfowl were in great abundance." "They blackened the sky like a cloud." "The valleys were teeming with waterfowl." "As we passed through resting flocks of geese, the birds were wholly unafraid, like barnyard ganders." In addition, there was a multitude of year-round birds of great variety, including resident nesting waterfowl.

Proof of the abundance of birds in the valley may be found in the clothing, ornaments, household items, and ceremonial costumes of the Maidu. Native Americans throughout the rest of California used animal skins and woven strips of skin, primarily rabbit, for such items. This was not so in the Sacramento Valley, where birds were more numerous than rabbits and more easily caught than big game. The Maidu made some winter coats and blankets from strips of rabbit skins that were left to dry in the sun, but they mostly used strips of feathered bird skins to fabricate warm mantles, capes, coats, and blankets for personal and family use.

The Maidu stuck feathers from large birds in their hair for ornamentation. Women wore earrings of bird bones with pendants fashioned from feathers. Initiation of boys included perforation of the septum of the nose through which, for the rest of their lives, they wore a feather, a pair of feathers, or a feathered

Hen Mallard and Brood
Mallards were historically—and are still—the most numerous of the nesting waterfowl in California.

stick. For the many rituals and ceremonies, feathers were used extensively to make beautiful capes, skirts, head coverings, belts, earrings, and other items. One source describes a striking ceremonial belt of red woodpecker and green mallard feathers. Feathers from smaller resident birds were used extensively, particularly for blankets, mats, and clothing.

Although the Maidu were plentiful and were concentrated in the valley, they would not have had a significant impact on the huge population of wintering waterfowl. Other sources of food were available, and there was little need to harvest more wildlife than was required to fulfill basic needs. Because intertribal relationships, including commerce, were minimal or nonexistent, each tribe found sustenance primarily from the immediate surroundings.

The Maidu were also adept in turning the abundant vegetation into clothing, baskets, mats, and cordage. From the strong cordage, they made dip nets, seines, nooses, fan nets, and drop nets. Rabbits and other small animals were driven into long nets and clubbed. Small birds were captured in great numbers by nooses and nets. A noose, with bait, served to trap ground birds such as quail. Some ducks, geese, pigeons, and crows were caught with nets. Waterfowl were also captured by a series of nooses stretched across a stream. A lone hunter lured geese under a net with a

Riparian Habitat
Wild grape draped over cottonwood and sycamore trees was common in the Sacramento Valley along rivers and streams and around ponds. The Maidu made good use of these areas in the summertime, as did native grizzly bears in fall and winter.

Tule Swales

Innumerable low marshy areas, choked with tules or cattails, were spread throughout the Sacramento Valley. Historically, the "early birds"—waterfowl migrating southward before the first fall rains— used these river and creek oxbows for loafing and feeding. Waterfowl arriving later dispersed through- out the floor of the valley as the swales and vernal pools filled up. These areas supported many other migrating birds and were also important year-round habitat for resident animals such as beavers (above right). This tule swale west of Richvale in Butte County (above), about one hundred feet wide, was photographed from the air in January 1984. It has since been filled and leveled for agricultural use.

live decoy, then pulled a string to drop the net and trap several birds. Nets hung over a pond bank caught feeding ducks at night when the birds touched the releasing strings.

From the valley waters, the Maidu took fish, river mussels, eels, crayfish, and other creatures. One of their most important food sources was salmon, harvested in great numbers during upstream migrations. The salmon were dried and stored for future use. The staple of the Maidu diet was acorn meal, made from the bounteous crops of acorns from the huge oak groves dotting the valley, primarily valley oak and live oak. Maidu women and girls hulled, dried, ground, sifted, and leached the acorns to produce the meal. It was then turned into gruel or soup to which dried or fresh fish, fowl, or other meat, as well as dried berries and seeds, might be added. A soft bread was also made from acorn meal.

For sanctuary during the winter, the Maidu sought out the Sutter Buttes. Old caves and grinding bowl areas remain there still, silent witnesses to the Indians' winter sojourns. The floor of the Sacramento Valley was flooded every other year or so as the Feather, Yuba, and Sacramento Rivers overflowed. During January and February of 1833, the Maidu were joined by John Work's Hudson Bay Company brigade. His journal tells of the winter rains and surrounding high flood waters that drove the valley's land animals into the buttes. On February 23, 1833, Work wrote: "We have been a month here and we could not have fallen on a better place to pass a part of the dead winter season when nothing could be done in the way of trapping on account of the height of the waters. There was . . . abundance of animals for our people to subsist on, 395 elk, 148 deer, 17 bears and 8 antelope have been killed."

As more white men came into the valley, their accounts confirmed the wide variety of wildlife species. Tule elk were common in the lowlands, antelope lived in the grasslands, and deer frequented the woodlands along the streams, as did grizzly bears during winter and spring. Beavers, mink,

ringtails, and river otters lived along streams and in the adjacent riparian environment. Jackrabbits, gray foxes, badgers, ground squirrels, and coyotes also thrived in the valley.

The demise of the native peoples of California is a sad story. The most devastating causes were white man's diseases, particularly smallpox, malaria, and syphilis, brought into the valley by the Hudson Bay and American

Indian Stones

These stones, undoubtedly the work of the Maidu, were found on Gray Lodge within the top twelve inches of soil. Most likely, they were used as weights for fish nets or for throwing thongs. To make the thongs, three or four stones were tied together on the ends of straps or strings. Geese were so abundant that it would have been easy for the Maidu to get close to flocks and throw the weighted thongs, encircling the necks of their prey.

According to early reports and journals, vast herds of tule elk made active use of Central Valley marshes and wetlands. John Work, Hudson Bay Company trapper, noted that his hunters killed 395 elk during the month they spent in the Sutter Buttes in 1833. The elk population was rapidly depleted by settlers, gold seekers, and market hunters who sold elk at the mining camps and elsewhere. This photograph was taken in 1927 by Joseph Dixon of the University of California.

trapping brigades during the 1830s. John Work recorded malaria in his party while they were still near what is now Walla Walla, Washington, and he continued to make note of members falling ill with the disease as they progressed southward through California. Native Americans had no immunity to these diseases. There are many records of coming upon Indian villages strewn with dead bodies, no one left living.

Settlers not only brought diseases that killed the native people but shot the Indians outright, believing them to be a "potential threat." The facts, however, were otherwise: Jedediah Smith, who worked his way up the Central Valley in 1827, found the native people to be almost universally friendly, and John Work, who frequently met them during his travels in 1832–33, wrote that they were "civil" and "mild-mannered." Thereafter, the introduced diseases, the slaughter of wildlife, the usurpation of land rights, and the dastardly conduct of early trappers, hunters, and settlers continued to decimate the California Indians. Historically, the statewide population of Native Americans was estimated to be 130,000. By the 1850s, it had dropped to only 15 to 20 percent of that figure—and was continuing to decline.

Black-tailed Jackrabbit

The first trappers in the valley recorded the abundance of jackrabbits and noted the Indians' use of rabbit fur for clothing, ceremonial robes, and blankets. In the 1880s, the Butte County towns of Gridley and Biggs held competitive hunts to cull jackrabbits feeding on grain fields. Jackrabbits are still common in the valley.

Ringtail

The fur of these mammals, especially the tail, was of value to early settlers. But since ringtails are secretive and hard to find, the high price did not compensate for the time and effort required to trap the animals.

THE BIG-GAME SPECIES—deer, tule elk, pronghorn antelope, and grizzly bears—did not fare any better than the Native Americans. Settlers began to move into the valley by the 1840s. Then, in 1849 and 1850, over a hundred thousand gold seekers came to California, all needing food. Tule elk provided choice meat and were easy to hunt, easier than the faster antelope. By 1870, but maybe as early as 1860, big-game animals of the valley, except for deer and a few antelope, had been wiped out by market hunters supplying the mining camps and city dwellers and by settlers engaged in subsistence hunting. The last sighting of antelope in Butte County was near Wicks Corner, eight miles northwest of Oroville, in 1889. By 1900, few deer remained, having been hunted not only for meat but also for hides. One example: In 1880, a glove factory in Red Bluff purchased over thirty-five thousand deer hides for fifty cents each from shippers in Shasta, Trinity, and Siskiyou Counties. The few hunting laws on the books were rarely enforced until after 1907, when the state's first hunting license law was enacted. The hunting fee was one dollar. Almost $100,000 was collected that first year.

In the 1870s, after most of the large mammals were killed off, market hunters switched to waterfowl and other bird species of the Sacramento Valley's wetlands, such as sandhill cranes, herons, egrets, and various shorebirds. By the 1880s, market hunting for waterfowl had become big business. The tularies of the Butte Sink, between Gridley and Colusa, north and west of the Sutter Buttes, became major hunting grounds for waterfowl marketeers. In his *History of the Sacramento Valley*, Joseph McGowan wrote: ". . . on one occasion, over ten thousand ducks reached San Francisco in a single day. Four companies sold almost two hundred thousand ducks in the San Francisco market in the 1910–11 season, but unofficial estimates place the total number reaching San Francisco that season at over five hundred thousand."

Waterfowl arrived in the fall in vast numbers, and the supply initally seemed endless. But, in time, unregulated hunting by marketeers, goose herders, gun clubs, and the general population—along with the loss of nearly 75 percent of wetlands habitat—coincided with a noticeable decline in the waterfowl population. Finally, in 1918, federal laws were enacted that prohibited market hunting of migratory waterfowl. This was further enforced in California by state law in 1923.

Although market hunting became illegal, it remained a means of livelihood in many farm communities throughout the state. This was especially so where cattle, rice, or dry-land grains were the main crops. One such area was around the town of Gridley in Butte County. I first became aware of the magnitude of illegal market hunting of waterfowl in the fall of 1947 when I became manager of what was then called Gray Lodge Refuge. The nighttime shooting within a few miles of Gray Lodge

Club Shooting in the Butte Sink
Members of the West Butte Sink Gun Club posed for a portrait in 1916. Although they were not market hunters and market hunting was still legal, they likely followed the practice of the time. Each hunter shot a full fifty-bird limit. If a hunter was a good shot, he helped his less-skilled buddy finish out his limit. Members took what they wanted for personal use and left the rest for the caretaker to sell to help pay for club costs. The birds shown here are almost exclusively mallards, the favorite duck of many hunters.

almost sounded like a war in progress. From November through the winter months, I knew that it did not come from farmers trying to keep birds off the crops, as almost all the rice had been harvested by then.

I talked to local wardens, rode with them on night patrol, and realized there really was a war going on—a war against ducks. It was alarming to learn that "market hunting" was still so prevalent almost thirty years after it had been outlawed. I felt I should be doing something about it, but was informed, rightly so, that my province was within the borders of Gray Lodge. I could arrest anyone breaking the law there; outside the refuge, enforcement was the responsibility of the wardens.

It was easy to kill ducks in large numbers at night when they were feeding. This was especially true on moonlit nights. Local violators were fully aware of this and knew that, if they were cautious, chances of getting caught at night were slim. It was a good full-time or part-time winter occupation. Illegal market hunters could get 250 or more birds in a drag and then sell them at $1.00 to $1.25 per duck. They made two drag hunts per week, which was hard work, particularly when fields were wet and adverse weather prevailed. A gunnysack packed with thirty dead, wet ducks weighed seventy-five pounds or more. A successful 350-bird drag would require three poachers to make three or four trips each. It was an activity for relatively young men.

In the late 1960s, I sought out old-timers for historical information about the area west and southwest of Gridley, particularly those parts that had been added to the refuge. One day, in the 1970s,

Goose Pits

This photograph shows legal market hunting from goose pits in 1914 in southwestern Butte County. Already downed geese have been propped up for use as decoys. These hunters also employed live decoys, undoubtedly pinioned. The dirt from the hunters' pits had been removed from the area to avoid alarming the incoming geese.

Market goose hunters in 1916 have brought pinioned geese in cages on the back of a wagon. They have gathered already killed birds to be loaded under the cages before they collect their pinioned birds.

I was talking with an older man who leased and managed waterfowl hunting rights on local ranches. He was also a guide and a very good caller, particularly of geese. He started telling me about his younger years as a market hunter. I asked if I could tape an interview, and he agreed. Word got around that I wanted to tape interviews, and I was surprised at the volunteers, who, twenty-plus years later, felt no fear or compunction about relating their illegal market-hunting experiences. There had been little or no community censure of illegal market hunting, and most of the ex-poachers were respected citizens.

One ex-poacher described a typical duck drag: "You would locate where a concentration of ducks had been feeding the night before—get there a little before they come in to feed. As they feed, they raise up and develop a leap-frogging roll as they move along in feeding out a field. You get up so that when that roll comes within range, you are shooting down that roll. The important thing is to get the right distance on the first shot. You whistle or make some noise so they throw their heads up to become better targets. That first shot has got to be just a little further beyond. By holding up over their heads, the bottom part of your shot pattern makes a swath through the birds. It's a science, getting them lined up for a big kill. . . . After the first shot, when you shoot with their heads up, they then jump up to fly, so your second shot is fired into them when they are about six feet high. You make the shot just over their heads again so as to get the pattern through them as they come flying up. By your third shot, the birds are just a solid mass that blocks the sky; your next shot would blast a big hole in [the flock] and you then keep shooting until your gun is empty."

He reported that one night, in one drag shoot, he and two other poachers killed nearly 900 ducks, the most they had ever killed. Another former market hunter made a drag alone and killed 387 ducks. Generally, two separate drags were made before the birds were taken to market. An average sale would be about 450 ducks, with maybe 10 extra thrown in to compensate for badly shot-up birds.

Similar stories could have been told all over the Central Valley. Illegal market hunters were in high gear wherever waterfowl concentrated in the winter months. Up until the mid-1950s, the estimated annual illegal kill in the Gridley area was eighty thousand birds; for the Sacramento Valley as a whole, more than a quarter of a million birds.

After a successful drag, the ducks were gathered up and taken to a secluded area, usually a ranch barn, where the entrails were drawn. The birds were hung in pairs along timbers or on a line to dry out the insides. About two days later, the ducks were placed in gunnysacks, thirty birds to a sack, and transported to market. Major markets were restaurants in Sacramento, Oakland, and San Francisco and steamship lines in the Bay Area. One pair of outlaws sold twelve hundred ducks at one time to San Francisco markets.

During the fall and winter months, when migrating waterfowl filled the valley, my staff and I maintained an active patrol around the boundaries of Gray Lodge and felt sure that no illegal market hunters ever invaded the area. Imagine my surprise and chagrin when I learned many years later during my interviews that this was not so. A duck-banding project was in progress on Gray Lodge by 1950. Shortly after the Rising

Ducks Leapfrogging
Working in a forward motion across a field, ducks clean out a spot, then lift up to move on to the next feeding area. These ducks are in the process of executing that move. Market hunters called this maneuver a roll. As the birds lifted to move their feeding line ahead, the hunters shot into the dense concentration of birds.

River Ranch was added to Gray Lodge in 1952, some banding traps were placed in ponds on the eastern border, about four miles from staff headquarters and residences. Ducks feed mostly at night, the best time to pull the birds into the baited banding traps, and it was usually midmorning before the banding crew reached the east-side traps to band and release captured birds. From one of the individuals I interviewed, I learned that he had participated in regularly raiding these traps. The poachers were smart enough not to raid the traps every night. They were also smart enough to leave eight to ten birds, so the banders thought that night's catch was slim. The raiders timed their steal for about sunrise or before. The former poacher told me, "When we took the first ducks from the traps, we wrung their necks to kill them. We had trouble selling the birds because the buyer in San Francisco didn't like purchasing ducks that had no sign of being shot, suspicious that the birds might have died from some disease." From then on, the raiders hung the birds along a fence line and shot into the already dead birds.

Why did so many men get involved in illegal market hunting? The main reason was the good, quick money. The ducks and geese were easily available in large numbers. There was little community stigma or disapproval for taking the birds illegally. Violators who were caught paid low

Banding Traps

Ducks do most of their feeding at night, the best time to catch birds in baited traps by biologists intent on attaching leg bands. Traps near the east border of Gray Lodge were regularly raided by poachers in the 1950s.

fines, and most were set free if the case was tried before a local jury. Killing waterfowl lessened crop depredations, and most farmers allowed anyone to take birds on their land. Some farmers even provided shotgun shells. As my interviews progressed, it became evident that the thrill of this clandestine activity was as strong a motivation as the money. A sort of fraternity of these outlaws were regular patrons of Morris Brothers Bar in Gridley during their active years, and they spent a lot of time there trying to out-brag one another. The old-timers I interviewed years later still enjoyed telling tales of how they outsmarted the wardens or about the times they almost got caught. A poacher who was successful at this game improved his bragging rights.

State and federal wildlife law officials battled hard against the illegal activity but faced an almost impossible situation. There were just too many violators for the number of enforcement officers. Most illegal market hunting of waterfowl occurred at night, when it was difficult to apprehend violators, especially for a warden working alone. There was little public support of wildlife laws, and wardens were seldom informed of known violations. Poachers kept close track of the activities and whereabouts of the local wardens and shared this information through an informal network. During these early years, the wardens were also hampered by lack of radio communication.

Diligent state wardens made a valiant effort to stem illegal market hunting, working on their own and with federal agents. Finally, the U.S. Fish and Wildlife Service, a federal government agency, decided it was time to get serious. In 1934, the service established a law enforcement office in Berkeley with Hugh Worcester in charge. His chief assignment:

Clean up illegal market hunting in California. After a year of surveillance and investigation, Worcester estimated there were at least 150 full-time waterfowl market hunters operating illegally in the state. He did not attempt to estimate the part-time poachers. Based on what I learned of the number of illegal hunters active in just the Gridley area, I believe that his estimates were very conservative.

From 1939 until the mid-1950s, Worcester's agents took twenty-six waterfowl-marketing cases into federal and state courts. Most involved restaurant owners or steamship lines in San Francisco, Sacramento, and Oakland and poachers from the Willows-Princeton area of the Sacramento Valley. For the next twelve years, many arrests were made by regular locally stationed federal game agents. None of this, however, seriously curtailed the poaching. One convicted violator claimed he had killed over fifty thousand ducks before he was caught. A Gridley man estimated that he alone killed over twenty thousand ducks each year during the late 1940s, including ducks killed while scaring, or herding, birds off unharvested crops for farmers, often for pay.

In Washington, D.C., top federal officials decided to make even more determined efforts to bring the illegal professional waterfowl marketeers

Four Wardens and 517 Ducks
The year was 1936. The place was an old barn where two illegal market hunters were arrested. The tally was 517 birds. The wardens waited in this barn near Gridley, Butte County, for sixteen hours before the hunters came to sack up the birds to take to market. The violators were later taken to federal court. The state Fish and Game wardens are, left to right, Taylor London, Al Tinnin, Fred Hecker, and L.W. Dinsdale.

in California under control. Several operations were set up in the state. In 1952, the U.S. Fish and Wildlife Service sent an undercover agent to Willows, where he established a home and a jewelry store. Operating under an alias, the agent was known by only three law enforcement officers in California. By late 1952, he had sufficient contacts to begin obtaining evidence against local violators. By the end of the following year, he had purchased ducks from twenty-two poachers in the Sacramento Valley and obtained evidence involving numerous nightclubs and taverns in the San Francisco Bay Area. Additional evidence was needed to complete many of the cases, so the federal government brought in another undercover agent.

The agents revealed themselves for the first time to California Department of Fish and Game wardens from the Sacramento Valley and held a briefing at the Sacramento Airport on February 27, 1954. By that time, the agents had purchased 4,760 ducks, kept in storage as evidence. Arrest warrants, search warrants, and detailed instructions for the Willows area operation were distributed to teams of officers. By 10 A.M. on the designated day, the teams had apprehended all twenty-two offenders. Simultaneously, twenty-nine men were arrested in Bay Area restaurants and markets for purchase of illegal ducks. All fifty-one were later convicted in federal court. The operation had been well coordinated, and the arrests received a lot of publicity. The Willows bust, plus other similar and continuing operations, effectively brought an end to illegal market hunting in California.

The diligence and determination of federal and state wildlife agencies made large-scale illegal market hunting a thing of the past. Other contributing factors were development of sophisticated techniques for wildlife agents and adoption of health regulations and inspections for establishments selling food for public consumption. Most encouraging of all was the renewed interest of many citizens in the plight of our wildlife resources.

THE DESTRUCTION OF NATURAL HABITAT as settlement and farming increased at the end of the nineteenth century had an even more dramatic impact on waterfowl. After the railroad from Red Bluff to Sacramento, via Chico and Marysville, was completed in 1870, towns such as Gridley and Biggs were established along the tracks as grain shipping points. Over subsequent decades and well into the next century, roads, bridges, levees,

Confiscated Guns
(LEFT)
In the efforts to stop market hunting, the U.S. Fish and Wildlife Service confiscated many illegal weapons. This photograph was taken at the service's Washington, D.C., office in the mid-1940s. Albert Day, chief of the service, who appears here, and his assistants were very helpful to the California Department of Fish and Game in promoting the first enlargement of Gray Lodge Refuge.

Confiscated Ducks (RIGHT)
In 1954, two U.S. Fish and Wildlife Service agents checked, counted, and labeled 624 ducks taken from illegal market hunters in preparation for a trial in federal court in Sacramento. The birds were stored in freezers until the case was brought to trial. After the trial, the judge determined how to distribute the evidence. Confiscated ducks were often donated to county hospitals or other public agencies.

and towns were built as people took over the valley. The gradual construction of water drainage and supply systems, the leveling of lands, and the intensive and extensive agricultural development, particularly for rice, left little native wildlife habitat in the Sacramento Valley area.

Alarming concerns for waterfowl populations were manifested by the mid-1920s, and conservation efforts began to emerge from the state government. The Gray Lodge Refuge, totaling 2,540 acres, was acquired by the California Division of Fish and Game in 1931. It was the first refuge established in the Sacramento Valley. Fortunately, the acquisition of Gray Lodge Refuge was only the beginning. From 1937 to 1989, the U.S. Fish and Wildlife Service established six waterfowl sanctuaries in the upper Sacramento Valley: the Sacramento National Wildlife Refuge in 1937; the Colusa National Wildlife Refuge and Sutter National Wildlife Refuge in 1945; the Delevan National Wildlife Refuge in 1962; the Butte Sink National Wildlife Refuge in 1980; and the Sacramento River National Wildlife Refuge in 1989. Not only did these areas provide habitat for waterfowl, but they also protected many other wildlife species.

Huffman Rookery

A grove (below) that once stood on the William Huffman Ranch, four miles northeast of the Gray Lodge Wildlife Area, provided one of the largest nesting rookeries in the upper Sacramento Valley. The area held thirty valley and live oak trees, as well as abundant blackberry vines, poison oak, and elderberry plants. When I took the photograph below in 1954, I counted roughly four hundred nests. Snowy egrets (above left), great egrets, great blue herons, black-crowned night-herons, crows, and yellow-billed magpies all nested there. Turkey vultures roosted in the grove, and California quail nested on the ground. Old-timers reported that this rookery was known to have been active as far back as 1870, when the town of Gridley was established. In 1957, the grove was demolished and the land prepared for rice farming.

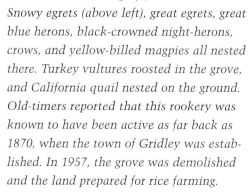

*These rice fields near
Richvale, between Chico
and the Sutter Buttes,
show the extensive
changes that clearing
and leveling land for
modern large-scale
agriculture brought to
the Sacramento Valley.*

Since that time, the California Department of Fish and Game has purchased lands between Gray Lodge and Chico: the Little Dry Creek Unit in 1989 and the Howard Slough and Llano Seco Units in 1992–93. Collectively, they are called the Upper Butte Basin Wildlife Area. The U.S. Fish and Wildlife Service has also purchased portions of the former Llano Seco land grant area, which are under the management of the Sacramento National Wildlife Refuge Complex.

Vast environmental changes have occurred in the beautiful, bountiful Sacramento Valley of the Maidu Indians, and we can never restore it to the way it once was. But efforts have been made to preserve parts of the valley, notably through the acquisition of Gray Lodge and its five additions, along with several other state and federal wildlife areas, and through extensive restoration on private lands. Protection of water rights and continued public resource management are vital to the survival of the remaining Sacramento Valley wildlife.

Cow Pasture to Marshland

S urely the Maidu Indians were fascinated by the millions of birds that flew in from the north to fill the Central Valley in the fall and then, just as mysteriously, flew back north in the spring. Where did they come from? Where did they go? The answers to these questions were reflected in Maidu folklore and religious ceremonies. Spanish missionaries, trappers, gold seekers, settlers, and all who followed must have been equally puzzled as they came into the valley. Scientific answers began to emerge by the early 1900s as bird-watching groups, educational institutions, and others in the United States and Canada experimented with various methods for tracking bird flights and migrations.

Bird banding proved to be the most successful technique. In 1920, most of the information gathered by various groups was turned over to the U.S. Bureau of Biological Survey, forerunner of the present U.S. Fish and Wildlife Service, and the federal banding program was officially begun, with biologist Frederick Lincoln in charge. By the mid-1930s, Lincoln had enough band returns to publish his concept of waterfowl migration in the United States. Based on his information, the U.S. Fish and Wildlife Service established four geographical

Refuge Enhancements
(OPPOSITE)
During my thirty-two years at Gray Lodge, many improvements were made to support wildlife. A dirt mound left from the construction of a pothole pond in the 1950s (inset) was planted with quailbush, which covered the mound by 1988. A pair of gray foxes built a well-hidden den under the bushes. The pond provided food and cover for wood ducks, cinnamon teal, and other birds. Shallower ponds maintained on the refuge were used by migrating dowitchers (above), yellowlegs, and other shorebirds.

areas as the primary migration routes of North American waterfowl: the Pacific, Central, Mississippi, and Atlantic Flyways. Continuing research has shown that breeding grounds and migration routes overlap more broadly than was originally thought. Nevertheless, although these flyway designations are not clearly definitive, they still serve well as waterfowl regulatory areas in the United States.

In 1928, the California state legislature passed an act providing for the acquisition of waterfowl refuges, and a portion of the state hunting license fee was designated for these purchases. Three years later, the California Division of Fish and Game established Gray Lodge Refuge, the first waterfowl sanctuary in the upper Sacramento Valley, in the heart of the Pacific Flyway waterfowl wintering grounds. The excellent location was probably due more to good luck than to careful study. The sixty members of the 2,540-acre Gray Lodge Gun Club located in southwest Butte County were in a quandary: their gray lodge building had burned down, and with the Great Depression in full swing, they had no funds to replace and maintain it. Since the members did not see eye to eye on several counts, they put the club up for sale.

Refinement of the flyway concept, accumulation of population counts, study of migration patterns, and other research were meager or did not yet exist, but it didn't take a genius to figure out that this acreage was an ideal location for a waterfowl refuge. The west boundary adjoined the Butte Sink, one of the several remaining freshwater marshes in the state; the south border was only one mile from the

Gray Lodge Gun Club

The club was organized in 1921 when land was purchased and a hunting lodge was constructed. Most of the members were from Marysville and Sacramento. Eight years after the club's founding, the lodge burned down. It was never rebuilt, and in 1931 the land was willingly sold to the State of California for the first waterfowl refuge in the Sacramento Valley.

Sutter Buttes

The Sutter Buttes are practically in the front yard of Gray Lodge Wildlife Area. When I moved to the area with my family, the buttes became very special to us. Their appearance changed with the time of day, with the time of year, with the weather. The best season of all is winter, when the abundant waterfowl add life and beauty to the view of this little mountain range.

foot of the Sutter Buttes. In the end, Gray Lodge was a decidedly wise purchase.

The development from an old gun club to the present-day 9,200-acre Gray Lodge Wildlife Area reflects the evolution of wildlife conservation and management during those years. The Gray Lodge Gun Club had always leased out cattle-grazing rights on the property. For this reason, the entire area was fenced. Some smaller sections were in turn cordoned off and leased for hay production. The many years of cattle grazing had kept the vegetation, including willow and cottonwood seedlings, down almost to ground level. The pasture received limited summer irrigation. A few levees built on the west side allowed the gun club to flood six hundred to eight hundred acres each hunting season with drain water from the Reclamation District Canal 833 via a diversion dam on the north side.

For the first two years, the state hired an off-site caretaker and continued leasing cattle-grazing and farming rights. The first manager, Lawrence Cloyd, was assigned there in 1933. That same year, the landmark

Gray Lodge
Headquarters
*This photograph
was taken in
January of 1984
from an elevation
of about five hun-
dred feet, looking
northeast. The
sanctuary and
visitor's route
are to the left.*

book *Game Management*, by Aldo Leopold, was published. Leopold felt strongly that humans could and should manage and develop land in order to preserve and enhance wildlife. That concept took some time to spread to federal and state agencies across the nation, and did not begin to filter down to Gray Lodge until Larry Cloyd's last years as manager. Even then, he was hampered by lack of funds, manpower, and equipment. His staff consisted of two men classified as "conservation aides." A good portion of his funds had to be used to set up an electric generator plant, plus a shop and storage buildings and a manager's residence. Later, levees and concrete water-control structures were built on the west side. The present three-mile visitor's loop road through the west-side sanctuary is atop one of those levees. He also managed to get electricity and phone lines to Gray Lodge before he left. Cloyd moved on from Gray Lodge to become my immediate supervisor, among other duties. He ultimately became deputy director of the California Department of Fish and Game.

My first work experience at Gray Lodge Refuge was in 1947 while assigned to the California Fish and Game Pheasant Research Project in Chico. We conducted pheasant nest surveys

New Job, New Uniform
(OPPOSITE)
*After graduating from
Sacramento Junior
College in 1938, I
joined the California
Division of Fish and
Game as an Assistant
Fish and Game Warden.
On completion of my
training, I donned the
uniform worn by all
new wardens in the
late 1930s.*

Lawrence (Larry) Cloyd was the first manager of Gray Lodge. His tenure began in mid-1933 and continued until October 1947, when I was appointed to take his place. Capable and conscientious, Cloyd did well with limited funds and manpower. He had a successful, fruitful career in the California Department of Fish and Game, retiring as the department's deputy director.

and brood counts on Gray Lodge in the spring of that year. I enjoyed hiking the area and was surprised by the diversity of wildlife that I observed during the surveys. I readily accepted the position of Gray Lodge manager when it was offered to me in September 1947 and moved to the area with my family in November of that year. I went to Gray Lodge thinking of myself primarily as a biologist. I was excited at the thought of identifying resident wildlife, conducting population and nesting studies, and researching individual species. Some of these activities I was able to accomplish in the early years, but I soon realized that I had to wear many hats: land developer, water engineer, farmer, office manager, personnel supervisor, budget developer, report writer, public relations officer, and educator, among many others.

From 1931 through 1952, Gray Lodge was maintained as a sanctuary, a refuge where waterfowl could feed and rest without intrusion or disturbance. No public access was allowed until after the visitor's loop road was built late in Larry Cloyd's tenure, though public access remained limited and very controlled. Hunting was not permitted until 1953. When I took over at Gray Lodge, visitors were required to stop at headquarters, check in, and leave their shotguns at the office while they proceeded around the west-side loop road. I enforced this regulation that first fall but discontinued it before the next hunting season. The office was in our residence, and my wife felt uncomfortable accepting and returning guns when I was busy out on the property. Besides, there were never any incidents with visitors shooting on the pond areas, and the only road out of the refuge went right through headquarters.

Another area of concern was the refuge boundaries. In winter, my staff of two men and I spent many of our working hours patrolling the boundaries, particularly on weekends. Much of the area did not yet have perimeter roads, and we did our best to let hunters, legal and illegal, know

Willow Pond

An area near the original Gray Lodge entrance was once a sand and gravel pit used by the Gray Lodge Gun Club. After I became manager, the last of the usable gravel was removed, and the pit was opened up to create a pond (left). In 1966, what we called Willow Pond was doubled in area and deepened to six to eight feet (below), enabling the water to stay cool enough to support a fish population. The excavated dirt was used to elevate the adjacent ground, which was then enhanced with plantings of deep-rooted trees, such as cypress, along with volunteer cottonwoods and willows.

that we were out and about. Most patrolling was done in the cold early-morning hours of the weekends. The three of us took turns in an old pickup with no heater, the refuge's only vehicle except for an ancient dump truck. I usually did the early hours, four or five o'clock in the morning. Patrol duties became less difficult and more effective as perimeter roads were gradually completed, staff was increased, and we had more and better vehicles. Being out and about proved effective. When we did apprehend poachers, the procedure was to get their names and driver's and hunter's license numbers and turn the information over to the local warden, along with details of the infraction.

As we rode through the refuge, we did another sort of patrol. All of the adjoining ranches ran cattle and overgrazed their land. Looking over at Gray Lodge, the ranchers saw a lot of vegetation and good ground cover, excellent feed for cattle. It was amazing how often the border fences developed breaks. Sometimes twenty-five to thirty head of cattle might get a day or two of good grazing on the refuge before we spotted them and notified the owners to claim them. The gate across the entrance road had been removed after the state purchased the land for the refuge. The entrance was over a mile from headquarters. One time, as I was going out at dusk, I discovered the next-door neighbor driving his herd of cattle right through the entrance. I stopped, got out of the pickup, and said, "Tom, I'll help you drive them back." Soon after that, we built a cattle guard across the entrance. The cattle problem was mostly solved when the state bought up adjoining ranches to enlarge Gray Lodge in the early 1950s. Occasional "fence problems" continued on the east side up into the 1970s.

The original Gray Lodge office was in the manager's residence, in a room that would normally have been a bedroom, except that it had an exterior door. The office was furnished with a convertible couch and a desk, and it connected to a small bathroom. When Larry Cloyd showed me the office, he said, "This is also called 'Joe's Room,' and he comes and stays when he pleases."

I heard this with some fear and trepidation, but it turned out to be a plus. Joe Hunter was my boss, Chief of Game Conservation, in charge of the state's waterfowl refuges, game farms, deer management areas, and just about everything that didn't come under fisheries. He had been with the state fish and game agency since 1913, working up through many positions during a period of growth and change. The headquarters then was in the Ferry Building in San Francisco, but Joe didn't spend a lot of time there. He always wanted to be operating from firsthand information so he traveled almost constantly to the areas and programs under his jurisdiction. We never knew when he might show up for a day or two. I enjoyed hearing his tales of the early days and picking his brain. He was a crusty kind of man, but I came to know and truly appreciate him as friend and mentor. He kept coming to Gray Lodge even after he retired in 1952, and he was always welcome. Joe lived to be ninety-three years old. During the last few years of his life, his son drove him up from San Mateo each fall after the birds were on the refuge. Probably no one ever has had or will have the feeling for Gray Lodge that I have, but Joe Hunter was a close second.

BECAUSE OF THE CALIFORNIA CLIMATE of mild winters and warm, dry summers, plus the abundance of water for irrigation, rice had frequently been suggested as a viable crop. Many attempts were made to grow rice, mostly in Central and Southern California, but they were never successful.

Tundra Swans in Rice Field
Most tundra swans arrive in the Sacramento Valley after the rice is harvested and therefore have only a minor impact on crop depredation. They glean the waste rice and pull up the roots as well.

Waterfowl Feeding

After only three or four rest stops during migration, ducks arriving early to the Sacramento Valley were hungry. An unharvested rice field was tempting, particularly if it had standing water. Beginning in 1948, a rather primitive method was employed to help ease this depredation problem. Bulk grains—wheat, rice, watergrass, and barley— were scattered from a pickup. Every year until 1954, when the practice ended, my staff and I put out over twenty pickup loads of grain. After Gray Lodge was enlarged, more than seventeen hundred acres of crops for birds were grown annually.

In 1908, a plot of experimental rice was planted on forty acres of adobe soil west of Biggs in Butte County. This crop matured and was the first rice harvested in the upper Sacramento Valley. By 1913, over five thousand acres of rice were planted in Butte County. Rice was also planted in Colusa, Glenn, and Sutter Counties.

Just at harvest time, millions of waterfowl migrated into the valley to spend the winter or pass through on their way south. Natural wetlands had been reclaimed for agriculture, beginning when the first settlers came to the valley, and successful rice production greatly accelerated the process. Waterfowl, particularly ducks, frequented the rice fields for food. A flight of ducks, leapfrog-feeding as they do, could roll right through a field in a short time. In 1917, losses from ducks and geese totaled three hundred thousand bags of rice, and a war of sorts began. In 1918, farmers armed themselves and their families and also hired employees with shotguns to scare off the birds. Many methods were used through the years to combat crop depredation by waterfowl: flares, fireworks, noise bombs, revolving searchlights, carbide guns. In 1948, Joe Hunter sent me down to Stockton to pick up a load of flares from an army surplus depot. Farmers applied to the local warden, who issued flare-launching rifles. Then they came to Gray Lodge, where I issued the flares. We did this for ten years or so. Another method—using light airplanes to herd ducks off the rice fields—proved to be effective but was costly.

By the late 1940s, rice production had increased to more than 250,000 acres, and rice growers demanded that federal and state agencies do more to alleviate the depredation problem. After considerable controversy and confrontation, it was decided that state and federal waterfowl areas should provide feed for birds arriving prior to rice harvest. The U.S. Fish and Wildlife Service brought in railcar loads of grain for bait feeding on the federal refuges and shared the grain with state refuges. We sent trucks to pick up the grain at the Sacramento National Wildlife Refuge and then spread it around the Gray Lodge ponds, a practice that continued acres of winter wheat and milo. The next year, 80 acres of millet were added.

These efforts did little, however, to alleviate rice depredation, and the clamor for a solution continued. Demand increased for more effort by the refuges to feed the early birds. Establishing additional refuges was considered, but met strong opposition from farmers in the areas under consideration. The opposition prevailed, yet the demand for feeding the birds continued. Finally, a decision was made to enlarge Gray Lodge Refuge. The acquisitions began in 1952, funded by the newly created state Wildlife Conservation Board, an entity charged with purchasing land for conservation and recreational purposes. Although providing more acreage for Gray Lodge seemed like a good solution, nearly 50 percent of the rice growers opposed the plan. Several well-attended hearings were held in Sacramento, some very hostile. Many rice growers thought that improving the refuge's habitat and growing crops on the refuge would pull in and hold more ducks in the valley and cause even more depredation. Others didn't want to see potential rice acreage absorbed into the refuge. Top U.S. Fish and Wildlife Service personnel from Washington, D.C., joined the California Department of Fish and Game staff, particularly director Seth Gordon, in support of the crop production and refuge enlargement plan. The plan was finally approved, by a small margin.

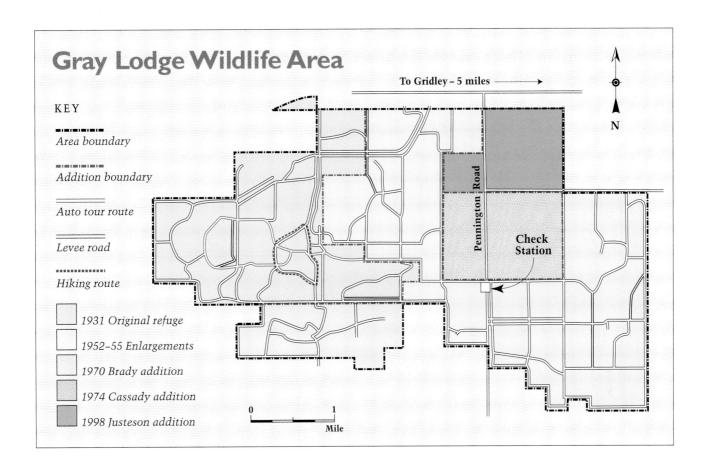

Gray Lodge Wildlife Area

N

KEY

▬▪▬▪▬▪▬
Area boundary

▬▪▬▪▬▪▬
Addition boundary

════════
Auto tour route

════════
Levee road

▪▪▪▪▪▪▪▪▪▪▪
Hiking route

☐ 1931 Original refuge

☐ 1952–55 Enlargements

☐ 1970 Brady addition

☐ 1974 Cassady addition

☐ 1998 Justeson addition

Pennington Road

Check Station

0   1
Mile

Between 1952 and 1955, Gray Lodge was enlarged by the acquisition of 4,160 acres of twelve separate adjoining farms and duck clubs, in twelve separate parcels. By late 1955, Gray Lodge Refuge totaled about 6,700 acres, and the name was changed to Gray Lodge Waterfowl Management Area. Our activities in the years that followed reflected the new name as we concentrated on intensive development, converting farmland into wetlands. Name changes through the years likewise represented changing emphases in purpose.

In 1970, the Marion Brady addition was purchased. This 760-acre parcel, located along the south boundary, contained several major drainage ditches with easements already connected to the Gray Lodge waterways. Water development costs, therefore, were relatively minor. The area's name was changed again, this time to Gray Lodge Wildlife Area, to mark the broadening of responsibility from protecting strictly waterfowl to conserving all wildlife. That name and purpose are still in place.

In 1974, the Cassady Brothers Ranch, almost 920 acres, was purchased. This brought Gray Lodge to 8,400 acres. The Cassady Ranch was bounded on three sides by Gray Lodge, and therefore ditches and roads could readily be tied into the refuge. One more addition has been purchased since I retired. The Justeson property, 780 acres in two parcels, was added in 1998. Both parcels were adjacent to Gray Lodge, separated only by bordering county roads.

AS EACH NEW ACQUISITION WAS MADE, I hiked the land and surveyed the property. What were the water sources? If there were none, how could we get water to the land? Where was high ground? Low ground? What kind of soils were we dealing with? What vegetation existed on the nonagricultural areas—abundant weeds, shrubs, or grasses, or scrubby, marginal plants? I could tell a lot by what grew voluntarily on an area. Prior land use, successful or not, also provided useful information.

Overall, with the new additions, Gray Lodge had a fairly good variety of soils. Three main types, loam, alkali, and adobe, could be identified easily. The best planting soil is loam, consisting mainly of sand, clay, silt, and organic matter. When cultivated, loam holds moisture well, thereby creating

Cane Clumps
Stands of cane ranging from five to twenty feet in diameter grow on various areas of Gray Lodge, particularly where the original Gray Lodge Gun Club had shooting ponds. Clumps are also found on many of the ranches that had leased out hunting rights and were later acquired to enlarge the refuge. The cane has little or no value for wildlife but is very difficult to eradicate. Although I wanted to remove the stands, I had more urgent work to do when I came to Gray Lodge.

good growing conditions. Most of the refuge's dry-land crops, shrubs, and trees were planted in this type of soil. Adobe soil characteristically has very high clay content and is the best for marshland as it holds water well when flooded. Beneath the adobe soil is usually a good layer of hardpan, a practically impervious, cemented layer eighteen to thirty-four inches under the topsoil. A few shallow loam areas of Gray Lodge also had a base of hardpan and therefore could be flooded successfully.

About 15 percent of the acquired land contained alkali soils. These soils have lots of mineral salts, such as calcium, sodium, magnesium, and

Multiflora Rose

Adobe soils crack open when dry and, as a result, lose moisture. Therefore, when we put multiflora rose (above) in adobe areas, we had to irrigate the plants until they became established. After that, they thrived and provided good escape cover for cottontails (right), California quail, and various sparrows and their broods. Multiflora rose was never planted near supply ditches, which had to be kept clear for fast and easy maintenance.

chlorides. Soils on some small ranches on the north side were almost all alkali. These ranches lacked access to irrigation district water, and only a couple had deep well pumps. The others were dependent on rainfall. Because most of the areas had not been leveled, ponds developed in many shallow basins during the rainy season. With the lack of runoff or drainage, whatever rain fell just dried up, leading over the years to a buildup of minerals in the soil. These areas were an advantage, as alkali ponds were favored by many species of shorebirds such as black-necked stilts, dunlins, dowitchers, yellowlegs, and avocets. Information about soil, as well as water sources both current and potential, were crucial in unifying all the separate properties into one wildlife area.

The Wildlife Conservation Board, which had funded the enlargements to Gray Lodge, had a threefold goal: 1) develop manageable marshland habitat; 2) develop fields and ponds for both dry-land and wetland crop production; 3) develop plans and facilities for public hunting. It was my responsibility to draw up the plans and budgets for accomplishing these goals on both the original acreage and the enlargements.

Fortunately, funds were provided by the board and the Pittman-Robertson Federal Aid to State Wildlife Restoration Act for the purchase of major equipment. We acquired heavy-duty tractors, dozers, graders, draglines, trucks, and forklifts from the Federal Surplus Property Equipment Program, which had an abundance of equipment left from World War II. The only cost was for transportation from the Army Supply Depot in Stockton to Gray Lodge. Our intensive habitat development project would have cost at least $2 million more and taken years longer had we been required to hire outside contractors. Pittman-Robertson funds also supported extra seasonal personnel during the period of intensive development.

With land, funds, and equipment in place, we went into high gear. For the next ten years, we worked steadily on water and habitat developments as well as on access roads and facilities for public hunting. At the same time, we were also growing crops to lure waterfowl away from rice-growing properties. Most summers, we ran double shifts seven days a week. Permanent staff was increased, which brought more families to live on the refuge. Two assistant managers were transferred to Gray Lodge when the state upland game farm program was discontinued—one to

The Right Equipment
Having appropriate equipment was crucial for converting farmland to wildlife habitat. Excellent heavy-duty World War II equipment was acquired through a federal program, and new machinery was purchased using funds from the Wildlife Conservation Board and annual Gray Lodge budgets. The staff and I felt like celebrating when we finally got this versatile backhoe. Here, it is being used to repair a corrugated metal pipe with a water-control riser for capturing water from a drain ditch.

supervise habitat developments and farming, the other to supervise development of facilities for public use. Three equipment operators, one equipment mechanic, two conservation aides, and one dragline operator were also added to the staff. Finally, in 1970, an office manager was hired. A good budget was allocated for summer and winter seasonal aides.

Water is the lifeblood of marshlands, and manageable water is a must if a wetlands ecology is to be created and maintained. Where possible, we maximized the use of free or inexpensive water. A major source of the former was Reclamation District Canal 2054, more commonly called Snake Creek, which ran along the southeast side of the Rising River area. This canal drained several areas north of Gray Lodge, and the district directors were happy to have additional runoff areas to help combat the winter flooding problem on Rising River and other areas to the south. Water could also be purchased from the Biggs–West Gridley Irrigation District at the northeast corner of Rising River.

The northwest corner of the original refuge was about six to eight feet higher than the southwest corner. Most ponds on the westernmost side of the refuge were constructed so that water flowed by gravity from the top pond down through each succeeding pond to the southwest corner of the refuge and out into the Butte Sink. Good marshland vegetation readily grew in these ponds.

In contrast, the eastern boundary of Rising River was about twenty feet higher in elevation than the west side of the original refuge. Therefore, a major ditch, about six miles long, was planned to flow, primarily by gravity, from the newly purchased east side to the far west side. This six-mile

Cassady Main Drain

After the Cassady Ranch was added to Gray Lodge in 1974, a major drain ditch had to be constructed to manage, disperse, and recapture water on this 920-acre property. Work was well under way in 1978 (left). Twenty years later (above), thistle had grown along the levee, providing nesting cover in the spring. In summer, the thistle seeds were eaten by mourning doves and many small birds. North Butte can be seen in the background.

water system would serve to capture most free, purchased, and pumped water from the east and central areas for reuse in the west side, as well as along the length of the system. Two primary types of pumps were needed along the way: ditch pumps, which lift low-level water in a ditch to flood or irrigate higher adjoining ponds and fields, and deep well pumps, some as deep as four hundred feet, which supply ground water to areas where no irrigation district or other water is available. Both pump types were also good insurance, providing a guaranteed supply of water for fall flooding and for habitat restoration and marshland maintenance. Irrigation and reclamation districts sometimes cut off water during fall and winter to conduct maintenance on their water conveyance systems. Water districts could also change the allocation and allotment of water.

Dragline Ditch Construction

The dragline was used to construct this ditch along the west side of the Cassady Ranch addition in 1974. When the ditch was completed, a pump at the high end of the ditch pulled in water and allowed it to flow, via gravity, and flood the field at right as needed. The ditch also served to recapture and reuse water from the flooded field. The dirt along the right side of the ditch was later compacted to create a levee road that provided access for pump maintenance, field operations, and recreational use.

Most ditch levees were developed as roads for public use or for maintenance and repair. Levees in a wildlife area have special requirements. The Gray Lodge levees had to be heavily compacted to withstand muskrat damage. We also built them wide to accommodate big equipment and to withstand washout and wind erosion, and made them high to allow for soil settlement. Good levees could be built from all Gray Lodge soils except alkali. When alkali soil gets wet, the minerals dissolve, and the levee turns to mush. In the alkali areas, soil was brought in to build the levees for ditches and ponds.

As we developed this major drain/supply system, we dug several pot-hole ponds, which became permanent ponds. It was a happy day when we

Ditch Habitat

Most ditches were dug a little wider and deeper than was needed to transport water, and they were also given sloped sides. This allowed riparian habitat to develop so that in fifteen years or so the ditches looked like natural streams. This is a photograph of one of those ditches taken in 1978, fifteen years after it was dug. Quailbush, fourwing saltbush, and multiflora rose had been planted along the left side; other plants are volunteer. A ditch that is held stable at three to four feet in depth, as this one is, retards the growth of tules and cattails, thereby minimizing maintenance. Fish, frogs, crayfish, snakes, and numerous invertebrates that serve as food for other marshland species use the habitat.

got our own draglines, which gave us the leeway to dig ponds when needed. Digging down to hardpan to obtain dirt for ditch levees left a good place for a pond that would hold water well. The best spots were where the water in the pothole would consistently be sustained by underground seepage from the adjacent ditch. In other areas, we put in a pipe from the ditch to maintain the water level.

At least twenty-six pothole ponds were developed, primarily for wildlife other than waterfowl. In time, these ponds provided habitat for aquatic vegetation and insects, fish, and other pond life that support a wide variety of birds, including black-crowned night-herons, bitterns, cinnamon teal, and wood ducks. Trees and other vegetation, and sometimes tules, readily grew around the edges to provide cover and, for some species, forage. The ponds allowed pheasants to bring their chicks to a safe place, just a short distance from their nest. I observed river otters feeding on the fish, primarily carp, in the potholes and was rewarded to see how wildlife used them as watering holes.

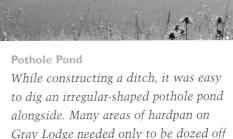

Pothole Pond
While constructing a ditch, it was easy to dig an irregular-shaped pothole pond alongside. Many areas of hardpan on Gray Lodge needed only to be dozed off and scraped to remove the topsoil and create a pond. Water for the ponds seeped in from the supply ditch alongside. The completed pond (above right) allowed pheasants with their chicks, as well as other water users, safe, easy access to water. Wood ducks (above left) and cinnamon teal liked these small ponds for breeding habitat.

Concurrent with water developments, we created one hundred field and pond areas. Almost all of these areas had water controls so each could be managed separately as a wetland pond or for dry-field operations. Because the ponds could be drained or filled one at a time for vegetation control, an entire marsh area never had to be completely drained again.

This was a lesson I learned early. When I first came to Gray Lodge, the tules had thrived to such an extent that much of the original sanctuary looked more like tule swales than ponds. Muskrats flourished and built big tule mounds in the ponds, filling much of what little open water was left. Muskrats had also done considerable damage to the levees. By 1950, my third year, I felt that repairing levees and clearing out tules should be the major summer work. As I started to plan the project, I realized that due to the existing gravity-flow water supply system, most of the ponds could not be managed separately. If a levee needed to be repaired or a clogged pond cleared of tules and cattails, the entire system had to be shut down and dried up. It became evident that we should make all improvements possible to the entire west-side water system.

The decision to dry up the area was not an easy one. Draining that much of the marsh at one time would have a negative impact on the resident wildlife, particularly the nesting species, and on beneficial aquatic plants. But we did proceed as manpower, equipment, and time allowed. After three summers, the ponds were clearer, and the water control system improved, though many areas of the refuge still could not be separately drained to do adequate marsh management or repair work. Thereafter, as

Cattails and Tules
These plants (above) are a mixed blessing in a marsh. Marsh-dependent species, such as black-crowned night-herons (right) and snowy egrets (far right), and many waterfowl use them as nesting sites. Cattails and tules also provide escape cover for wintering waterfowl. But excessive growth of the plants can choke out a pond and must be controlled to prevent the loss of open pond areas where essential wildlife plants grow. On a rotating schedule, we plowed the plants, turning up the roots so they would bake in the hot summer sun before flooding the field in fall for the returning waterfowl.

66

*Muskrats reproduce at a fast rate;
they have two or three litters per
year, averaging four to eight, with
up to eleven, young per litter. The
only advantage to having muskrats on a wildlife refuge is that
they like tules and sometimes eat
out a tule-clogged area, clearing
a pothole for waterfowl. But that
is not enough to counteract the
damage done to levees. Modern
engineering, however, can minimize muskrat damage to levees.*

Gray Lodge was enlarged, I kept this guiding principle in mind: Unless it cannot be avoided, never develop ponds or fields that cannot be flooded and drained independently.

It was also important to develop a rotating schedule of vegetation control in the ponds so the task would not be the major undertaking it was that first time. The schedule could not be rigid, however, as each pond had its own special problems and limitations. On a rotating schedule, we did tule-cattail control work on about three hundred acres each year—draining ponds, plowing, mowing, disking the fields—thus restoring open pond areas. If no control methods are used, tule-cattail monoculture can choke out other plants beneficial to waterfowl. Properly controlled, tules and cattails are vital to a marsh. Besides cover for many species, they provide nesting sites for snowy egrets, black-crowned night-herons, marsh wrens, and many other species.

What we had learned about ditch levees also applied to the smaller levees, called "field levees," that separated the many field and pond areas. Like the main levees, they were compacted well to discourage muskrats and ground squirrels. They were generally at least nine feet across to provide maintenance and public hunter access and to create hiking trails. Their height, about three to three and one-half feet, and their broad slope allowed the growth of grasses and forbs, which provided nesting, feeding, and escape cover.

Introduction of plants beneficial to wildlife, preferably native plants, was a priority. However, some native plants take a long time to reach a stage where they support wildlife. Therefore, I always maintained an open mind regarding the use of naturalized or introduced plants, as the plants that work best for wildlife should be used. Working with the Plant Introduction Station of the U.S. Soil Conservation Service (now the Natural Resources Conservation Service), we did final field-testing for plants identified as beneficial to wildlife. At Gray Lodge, we had success with California natives such as wild rose and two species of *Atriplex*, quailbush and fourwing saltbush. We extended the range of Arizona cypress and Nevada cypress, trees native to Southern California. Successful non-natives were the fast-growing multiflora rose, eucalyptus trees, and Russian olive trees.

Based on my decades of experience, I feel that primary attention in managing a refuge such as Gray Lodge should be paid to the needs of the large wintering waterfowl population. But since most of these refuges are considered wildlife areas in name or in mandate, providing food, water, cover, and space for resident species is vital. Although each area is different—and a knowledge of that area's particular wildlife and their relationships is essential to a refuge manager—I strongly believe that at least

Pied-billed Grebe Nest (OPPOSITE)
Keeping water levels stable during grebe nesting enhances nest success, as grebes almost always build a floating nest in water fourteen to sixteen inches deep. Some nests are free floating, like the one here; others are anchored to vegetation. All have little or no cover so the birds can dive off the nest directly into the water. The nest consists of a mass of aquatic material that, as it decomposes, probably keeps the eggs warm when the adults have to leave. When the birds leave, they often cover the eggs with nest material. Grebes are common nesters at Gray Lodge and throughout California's Central Valley.

Common Snipe
Favoring wet meadows, snipe are often seen alone and occasionally in small flocks. Although they can be hunted legally, the annual take at Gray Lodge during my tenure was less than two hundred per year, due primarily to the birds' zigzag flight pattern, making a successful shot difficult.

10 percent of an area should be maintained in permanent and semipermanent stable water, not including ditches, in order to sustain the populations of species that require year-round water. This is what we worked so hard to do at Gray Lodge.

To meet another mandate of the refuge — relieving rice crop depredation—more food crops had to be grown. The production of food crops for waterfowl was not unique to Gray Lodge. The Sacramento, Delevan, Colusa, and Sutter National Wildlife Refuges also went into full-scale farming. The Klamath Basin National Wildlife Refuge Complex, a key stopover area for migrating waterfowl, was farmed extensively in hopes of keeping the birds in the Klamath Basin longer before the final lap of their flight to the Central Valley wintering grounds.

When we first planted millet in the late 1940s, a beautiful, thick crop resulted, but the birds did not feed in the millet field. Puzzled by this, I drove out to watch birds feeding in rice fields. Then I took a crew with scythes to the millet field, and we cut out some millet to make open areas. The plan worked. The birds came into the newly formed ponds and cleared out the millet. Since millet grows in water up to four inches deep, leaving a few deep spots throughout the field formed small pothole ponds where the ducks could come in to feed. I also learned not to seed millet as heavily as we did initially. The next year, we also planted dry-land fields of wheat and barley. By the time the refuge enlargements began in the 1950s, about 600 acres of crops were being grown on the original 2,540 acres.

Our early experience taught us how easy it was to raise successful stands of millet. Millet matures in about seventy days and is less expensive than other grain crops. Millet will come up voluntarily in a field after fall flooding for two or three years in a row before reseeding is required. After Gray Lodge was enlarged, rice farmers thought rice would do a better job of pulling in the birds. We tried this in some of the former rice fields, but rice was much more costly, and the fields needed more preparation. Rice took up to 160 days to mature, twice as long as millet. Ducks like both crops equally. When waterfowl populations arrive in the fall, a very large percentage are young of the year and have never made the trek to Gray Lodge. Each year, I thought, why encourage them to like rice? After five years, we quit growing rice.

By the early 1960s, we were planting annually at least twelve hundred acres of millet in the spring as well as an average of three hundred acres of dry-land crops, primarily wheat and barley. Wheat and barley were planted in early fall so they were just sprouting to three or four inches when the birds arrived. This provided good

Sanctuary Pond

On this public hunting day in 1973, waterfowl were smart to seek refuge on a sanctuary pond. North Butte dominates the background.

Arizona Cypress Grove

The Gray Lodge habitat program aimed to support a variety of species by providing food, nesting habitat, and cover. Drought-resistant plants that required little care once established were given special emphasis during the field-testing done from 1960 to 1975 in cooperation with the U.S. Soil Conservation Service. Arizona cypress, native to Southern California, thrived when planted where loam soil was not less than three to four feet deep. This photograph (top left) shows a cypress grove thirteen years after planting. I was surprised to find barn owls (below left) using the trees; they probably liked the darkness among the inner limbs.

grazing for geese, wigeon, and coots. Some years, the birds didn't kill the crop but just clipped off the green shoots, and the crop often grew back thicker and better. Other plantings were timed so they would mature early enough to hold waterfowl on the refuge until after most of the rice was harvested. At the same time, the newly developed marshlands were maturing and providing more natural foods each year. We all felt satisfaction when the early waterfowl arrivals went readily to newly developed pond or crop areas.

Milo maize was the best multipurpose crop. It attracted blackbirds and starlings, which at times equaled or exceeded waterfowl in their ability to damage the rice crop. Milo in the dough stage, before it hardens, is like ice cream to these birds. Sandhill cranes, pheasants, and doves were also drawn to it. About one hundred acres of milo fields were scattered in

Hungry Pintails

These northern pintails, flushed out of a millet field where they were feeding, are evidence that we were successful in keeping hungry birds on the state and federal wildlife areas, rather than in the rice fields. To get this photograph, I stood at the edge of the field and clapped my hands. There were many more birds that ignored me. Millet became the major waterfowl food crop grown on Sacramento Valley wildlife areas.

patches of twenty to thirty acres each. Another one hundred acres of safflower, Sudan grass, field corn, and sunflowers were also grown in different years, in different amounts, to augment milo as a food for multiple species.

At the beginning of the twenty-first century, rice crop depredation by waterfowl is no longer a serious problem, due not only to the efforts of government wildlife agencies but also to those of the rice industry. The best way to cut down on rice crop depredation by waterfowl is to harvest the crop as early as possible, before the major fall migration. Several developments have made this possible. The Rice Experiment Station, near Biggs, California, began an accelerated research program in 1969 to improve rice varieties in California. The resulting semidwarf varieties have stalks up to twelve inches shorter than previously planted varieties and are less likely to fall over due to wind, rain, or grain weight. The new varieties are also easier and faster to harvest and have shorter maturity periods, averaging 130 days compared with 160. Peak harvest time is September 15 to October 15, sometimes stretching into early November, depending on the weather. In the early years of the refuge, farmers were sometimes still harvesting "Christmas rice" long after waterfowl had moved into the valley. A very significant factor in the faster, more efficient harvest of the rice crop is the sophistication of modern equipment. Rice dryers, also more efficient, have increased in number, whereas in the early days, growers sometimes had to delay harvest, waiting for a turn at a dryer. The practice of laser land leveling, which results in precisely flat land that requires less contouring with the small dams called rice checks, provides more land for crop production and allows more efficient water management. There is also more room for today's big harvesters to maneuver, contributing to faster completion of the harvest.

Sunflower Bird Seed

For a few years, we put in five-to-ten-acre plots of various plants to see how well they grew on Gray Lodge, how much care they required, and how well they were utilized by birds. We found that sunflower, safflower, Sudan grass, Mexican wheat, different milo maizes, and field corn all grew adequately or well on the area and were eaten by one or more species. However, milo was used by a greater variety of birds: pheasants, doves, blackbirds, starlings, sandhill cranes, passerines, and waterfowl. It was also easier and cheaper to grow. Thereafter, we concentrated on milo but continued to put in plots of other varieties when time, acreage, and budget allowed.

Visiting Bird-watchers

Many bird-watchers come to Gray Lodge, individually and in groups. This group came by bus from Sacramento, where they were attending a National Audubon Society convention in November of 1966. They were somewhat awed by the concentrations of waterfowl on the area. I developed a great respect for bird-watchers. Many were outstanding ornithologists, with very impressive life lists.

Another plus for wildlife in the Sacramento Valley is the phasing out of the burning of rice stubble. Rice stubble, unlike the stubble of most crops, does not readily decompose when plowed under. Burning of stubble in the fields had become an accepted method of straw management by the 1920s. It was fast and effective and also helped control diseases and pests. By the time I was back in the area after World War II, it was very evident when farmers were burning rice stubble: smoke filled the valley. As rice growing accelerated, the problem became worse and lasted longer. The first attempts to control burning were enacted by the state legislature in 1970. Finally, in 1992, the California State Air Resources Board issued an edict that would restrict the burning of rice stubble by 2001 to 25 percent, except for disease control under very strict proof and permit regulations. Even in 2000, when 29 percent burning was still permitted under the edict, few farmers burned due to rigid control of the days and weather when the practice was allowed.

To replace burning, growers reflood the rice fields after harvest. The flooded acreage benefits waterfowl by providing loafing and feeding areas, and the birds actually help break down the straw by walking on it through the winter months. In fact, some farmers get extra income by leasing hunting rights to their property. I am happy to say that relations between rice growers and government agencies responsible for wildlife are now quite amicable and cooperative.

WHEN THE WILDLIFE CONSERVATION BOARD approved funding for the refuge enlargements, part of the agreement was that portions of the refuge would be opened for controlled public hunting after the rice harvest was completed. This brought large numbers of visitors, who discovered that a swing around the sanctuary visitor's loop provided a spectacular sight. As habitat improvements were made, more and more people other than hunters and anglers became aware of Gray Lodge and the opportunity to observe wildlife, particularly birds. This led to the necessity to provide for a much greater number of year-round visitors, including individual birders and bird-watching groups, hikers, photographers, and groups of students of all ages. Dr. A. Starker Leopold brought his game management students from the University of California, Berkeley, every year until he retired, as did Dr. Stan Harris from Humboldt State University. Biology field trips from other colleges were also common. Annual Retriever Field Dog Trials were also conducted at Gray Lodge and continue to be held on the refuge. Gray Lodge served as a demonstration area for upper-echelon Department of Fish and Game people, who brought many national and international

Ansel Adams

Although he was not primarily a wildlife photographer, Ansel Adams brought small classes to Gray Lodge. I attended and appreciated an excellent week-long seminar he taught on black-and-white photography and development techniques at the University of California at Santa Cruz.

A. Starker Leopold

Dr. A. Starker Leopold, mentor and friend, brought his U.C. Berkeley wildlife management classes to Gray Lodge each year. We sometimes scrambled to find sleeping quarters for them, assigning some to the bunkhouse, others to the grain building, and yet others to the equipment garage. The visits were intensive, with lectures and hikes. I was always amazed at Starker's ability to identify birds on the wing, especially waterfowl.

delegates throughout the years. Public use grew to about eighty thousand visitors per year, including hunters and anglers, as the area was enlarged and developed.

As the number of visitors increased, coping with public use became a significant part of our duties. Staff were assigned to work with many visiting groups, and I spent much of my time meeting with groups of adults from the National Audubon Society and the Sierra Club, college classes, and other delegations. I always enjoyed sharing Gray Lodge. Expanded public use meant that we had to develop and maintain designated visitor areas, roads, parking areas, hiking trails, and restrooms, as well as signs, maps, and use regulations. Schedules for refuge personnel were rotated so staff would be available for weekend duty. Lists of birds, mammals, amphibians, and reptiles inhabiting Gray Lodge were printed for visitor use.

For many years, a pen with live waterfowl was maintained in the headquarters area, to teach visitors how to identify species. This was later replaced by a small museum containing mounted specimens, primarily birds, endemic to the area. Through the years, I had collected wildlife that had

The People Behind the Wheels
I share this picture with pride and affection. Taken in 1978, it includes most of the long-term employees who had a major role in the development of Gray Lodge during my years there. I am at the far left and had just completed 30 years as manager of the area. Next to me are James R. Wilson, 26 years at Gray Lodge; Barney Jacquot, 25 years; Morris Horn, 20 years; John Jacquot, 23 years; Steve Hrinsin, 17 years; and Myron Fountain, 10 years— for a total of 151 years of state service. These six conscientious, capable men could do many jobs and do them well. The photograph was taken by office manager Diane McCracken.

In November of 1966, the renowned artist, author, and birder Roger Tory Peterson (center) and Les Line (right), editor of Audubon *magazine, visited Gray Lodge while attending a conference in Sacramento. I joined them for a photograph taken by Lorna Hrinsin.*

Jack Paniyak

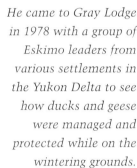

I met Jack in the early 1970s when I spent a week in the Yukon Delta. He came to Gray Lodge in 1978 with a group of Eskimo leaders from various settlements in the Yukon Delta to see how ducks and geese were managed and protected while on the wintering grounds.

succumbed on the area and, in the absence of money in the state budget for taxidermy, I personally paid to have the specimens mounted. Education groups especially found the museum useful.

The first wildlife research at Gray Lodge was the Pheasant Research Project, in which I participated. In 1948, I undertook a three-year nesting and productivity study of the western mourning dove. In 1952, headquarters for the pheasant project was transferred to Gray Lodge. The following year, the California Department of Fish and Game established a Field Research Station at Gray Lodge to support a statewide waterfowl studies project, as well as the pheasant project. Over the years, prime research projects on marsh management, habitat planting, upland game, snipe, and other subjects were conducted from this station. In addition, several studies by university and college master's and doctoral degree candidates were conducted on Gray Lodge in coordination with refuge staff.

Another major project was undertaken when I first came to Gray Lodge. The U.S. Fish and Wildlife Service coordinated banding and research activities in the lower forty-eight states, as well as on the Alaskan breeding

Retriever Field Dog Trials
For over forty years, field dog trials have been held on Gray Lodge, under regulated permit. The trials were fascinating to watch. The handlers and owners put a lot of time and dedication into the training of the dogs. This dog, having made a successful retrieve, is returning to its master. It belonged to a member of the Sagehen Retrievers Club. Such clubs proved to be among our best guests.

grounds. These activities, funded by the Pittman-Robertson Wildlife Restoration Act, were conducted by the fish and game agencies in each state. California's Pittman-Robertson Waterfowl Project 30-R, supported by the act, began in 1948, with permanent research headquarters established at Gray Lodge in 1952 and maintained there until 1983. The major purposes were not only to study migration routes but also to determine trends in mortality rates. The information gained was crucial for setting hunting seasons, bag limits, and species limits, and was also vital for identifying declining populations that should be more intensely managed. In California, waterfowl were banded at thirty different locations. About 80 percent of the banding was done at five locations: the Klamath Basin National Wildlife Refuge Complex, and Gray Lodge, Honey Lake, Los Banos, and Imperial Valley Wildlife Areas. From the start of the project through 1986, over 550,000 birds were banded, yielding over 86,000 band returns for California.

Of those more than 550,000 birds, 221,000 were banded by the late biologist Warren C. "Bud" Rienecker or were banded in his presence. Rienecker was assigned to the banding project in 1954 and was stationed at the Gray Lodge field office. In his thirty-three years with the project, he banded more waterfowl than any other person in North America and pioneered many banding techniques for Pacific Flyway waterfowl. Rienecker wrote at least thirteen research papers related to the banding project and its findings, giving the field a wealth of well-documented and analyzed data that still serve as the basis for waterfowl conservation and management.

By 1980, Gray Lodge had grown in many ways, from the overall size of the refuge to the number of annual visitors and the reasons they came to the refuge. Four residences, a research field office, a bunkhouse, a small museum building, and several equipment, storage, and garage buildings were all located around the headquarters office. Areas were designated for parking equipment and storing pipes, water controls, and bridging structures. Before I retired, an east-side subheadquarters had been established on the Rising River Ranch addition, including two residences, a large storage barn, two silos, and a storage shed. Draglines, tractors, bulldozers, backhoes, forklifts, land planes, mowers, grain drills, seeders—the equipment at Gray Lodge was too numerous to list. Nine permanent employees were on staff, assisted by numerous seasonal employees who worked primarily in activities related to public hunting and farming. Fourteen hundred acres were devoted to growing crops, with the remainder in permanent and seasonal ponds and upland fields.

But a list of tangible things cannot begin to express my appreciation for the opportunity I fell into at Gray Lodge. I was blessed to have been granted more than thirty-two years to learn and grow as Gray Lodge became what it is today.

Banding Trap
Biologists watch an area to see where waterfowl are working in order to choose a spot to put out traps. Here, several birds inside the trap have been driven into a smaller holding cage. The bander then reaches through a small side opening to bring out a bird for banding. Over seventeen thousand bands have been returned from ducks banded at Gray Lodge.

CHAPTER 4

Seasons of Birds

As Gray Lodge Wildlife Area was enlarged and additional habitat developed, the variety and quantity of birds frequenting the refuge increased. This increase brought bird-watchers to the area throughout the year, and they soon far outnumbered the wintertime hunters.

With the refuge attracting more and more bird-watchers, I wanted to provide visitors with a list of the species they could expect to see. For the first rudimentary bird list, I turned to my field notes and augmented them with notes from various other observers. The 1972 list consisted of 194 birds, including species deemed occasional, rare, uncommon, or accidental on the area. By 1979, most major habitat development had been completed, so I had time to update the list. It contained 205 species plus 21 accidental visitors, birds that may be seen but are far from the places where they naturally occur. The 2000 Gray Lodge list (see page 152), which also encompasses the Upper Butte Basin Wildlife Area, cites 206 species plus 32 accidentals.

Since 1948, the species observed at the refuge have waxed and waned in number. To this day, however, waterfowl—spectacular particularly in winter—continue to outnumber and outshine the other species. Many of the wintering ducks return north to nest in spring, while some stay behind to raise broods. A 1949

Great Blue Heron Nest (OPPOSITE)
This nest was one of twenty in a rookery in a grove of cottonwood trees on Gray Lodge. Black-crowned night-herons occupied the lower branches.

Ring-necked Duck (ABOVE)
These diving ducks winter where deep freshwater ponds are available. Although uncommon on the refuge, they showed up in hunters' bags when flood waters backed up into the adjacent Butte Sink area.

Hen Mallard (ABOVE)

Female mallards do not incubate eggs until the entire clutch is laid so all the eggs hatch at about the same time. When all the young are hatched and dry, the mother leads them to a pond where they feed on aquatic insects and are less vulnerable to predators.

Mallard Duckling (LEFT)

Ducklings like this little mallard move with amazing speed as they scoot over the water and into protective cover when an intruder or predator approaches. The hen mallard does a remarkable job of protecting and training her young after they hatch out. Mortality is high, however, primarily due to predation. If ten ducklings leave the nest with the mother, only about five or six will still be alive within ten to twelve days. In another four or five weeks, only four may be left.

census of ducks nesting on the refuge listed approximately five hundred pairs. At that time, few private gun clubs in the Butte Sink kept their lands flooded after hunting season. As more habitat became available elsewhere, the birds spread out and numbers of breeding ducks on Gray Lodge declined, averaging about three hundred to three hundred fifty pairs annually. This nesting population was made up of approximately 70 percent mallards, 10 percent gadwalls, 10 percent cinnamon teal, and 10 percent ruddy ducks, redheads, northern shovelers, and northern pintails combined. More and more private gun clubs are maintaining ponds during the spring and summer months, as studies have shown that such water is critical for resident duck nesting and also provides good natural aquatic food for ducklings. Late-summer flooded wetlands are important for supporting early-arriving migrating ducks. Ponds with a stable water level are especially crucial for feeding and protection during the nesting season and the annual molt of waterfowl. A few permanently flooded wetlands assure the special year-round requirements of diving ducks and redheads.

As the years went by, I found that I could only generalize about when and which birds arrived, as they did not necessarily show up in the same order or at the same time each year. Storms and temperatures largely determine departure times from the Klamath Basin. Populations of waterfowl in the Central Valley are in a state of flux throughout the fall. Some groups just stop over to rest and refuel before continuing south. Wintering birds do some exploring before they select their loafing and feeding areas. Waterfowl establish strong affinities for both nesting and wintering grounds. Following the first year of life, more than half of the waterfowl are returnees from previous years. Returning birds are quick to settle in and make Gray Lodge their winter home. Once they establish their feeding area, there is the daily coming and going as flights move out to feed and return to rest in safety.

Snow geese have always been the most numerous of the wintering geese on Gray Lodge. When I first came to Gray Lodge, white-fronted geese were next in numbers. Starting in the late 1950s and continuing to this day, the wintering population of Ross's geese has steadily increased, and they have become the second most numerous wintering geese. Smaller numbers of white-fronted geese and a few flocks of cackling Canada geese winter at Gray Lodge. I have only rarely seen Canada geese (honkers) on the area.

Drake Gadwall

Many people have difficulty learning to identify gadwalls. The drakes seem somewhat drab compared with the drakes of other species. The black rump area is perhaps the most distinguishing feature. In flight, the birds show a white patch on the hind edge of the wings, a whitish belly, and yellow feet. Gadwalls are regular breeders on Gray Lodge and throughout the Sacramento Valley. From the 1950s through the 1970s, twenty-five to thirty-five pairs nested annually on Gray Lodge.

Resting Waterfowl

Waterfowl do not seem to sleep. During the day, they loaf and rest. At night, they fly to feeding areas, returning in the morning to rest some more.

The first geese came down sometimes as early as late September. These were medium-sized flocks of white-fronted geese. Smaller groups continued to fly in until most had arrived by late October. During the 1970s and early 1980s, snow geese, Ross's geese, and Canada geese usually migrated south from the Klamath Basin in early November, depending on the weather up north. After 1970, they consistently began to come in about two weeks later, in middle to late November. The pattern of early arrival in the valley recurred in the 1990s. Weather patterns did not significantly change. Perhaps the shift in arrival time was because the Klamath Basin National Wildlife Refuge Complex was raising more food crops for waterfowl.

Visitors to the sanctuary see a lot of white geese. The different species sometimes intermingle, especially when they are aroused to flight, but snow and Ross's geese, as well as the white-fronts, usually congregate in separate roosting areas on the ponds. During my years at Gray Lodge, no geese stayed to nest. About a dozen birds crippled by shot during the hunting season remained behind each year but did not nest. They flocked up together and, some years, moved to the Butte Sink to join other groups.

Ruddies (top right) are small, easily recognized ducks that usually carry their short "stiff tail" up at an angle. When threatened, they dive underwater rather than fly away. I saw only four or five ruddy duck nests a year on Gray Lodge. The hen (bottom right) lays a particularly large egg for such a little duck, considerably larger than a mallard egg. There seems to be good pair bonding between male and female ruddy ducks. The male ruddy stays around and helps, even after the brood is hatched.

Cinnamon Teal

This species of teal seems to be less gregarious than other ducks. Spring flights of mated birds may include only a scattering of loosely connected individual pairs. Even in migration, they remain in relatively small flocks. Twenty to twenty-five pairs of cinnamon teal nested on Gray Lodge each year. I liked cinnamon teal, maybe because pairs seemed to show more devotion to each other than do other nesting ducks.

Cinnamon Teal Brood

During nesting, cinnamon teal generally confine their activities to rather small territories and prefer heavy ground cover near small ponds or bordered ditches. Feeding and loafing are all carried out in close proximity to the nest. Thus, the male can stay nearby and be watchful. The hen may well be the best of waterfowl mothers. She consistently keeps her brood near escape cover and, if threatened, diverts attention by feigning injury. When I neared this two-day-old brood, the mother gave a signal, then flew up in a half circle around me as the ducklings scurried into a little ball and remained motionless. I immediately left the area.

Snow Geese Sentinels (ABOVE)

Flocks of snow geese seem to have sentinels that protect the birds during resting periods. These geese, found on the outer edges of the flock, assume guardianship and look alert. This photograph was taken three weeks after the end of the hunting season, when the birds were a little less wary.

Snow or Ross's Goose?

Identifying these two geese is difficult, especially when the birds are in flight. The Ross's goose (right) is smaller than the snow goose (left), about mallard size. Most adult Ross's geese have bluish warts along the upper part of the bill. The bill of the snow goose is a little longer and has a black "grinning patch."

Snow Geese Concentration (BOTTOM RIGHT)

Geese pack in closer together than most other waterfowl. The flocks are drawn to several specific ponds on Gray Lodge.

White-fronted Geese

These were the first geese to arrive in the fall, usually from early to mid-September. The annual winter population on Gray Lodge seemed to fluctuate more than that of other geese, with a gradual decrease over the years that was reversed when Eskimos and California hunters came to an agreement to reduce the harvest of geese in Alaska and California.

Although geese migrate primarily at night, daytime flights are more common than with ducks. If geese sense arrival of inclement weather or when the Klamath Basin refuges experience a freeze, they head south day or night. Whereas ducks seemed to sneak in to Gray Lodge, geese always made their arrival known by their calling. They got noisier as they started dropping in, circling downward and sometimes doing a few flip-overs and side-slips to help lose altitude. I just had to stop and watch them. Some groups were quite large, made up of many separate flocks, and it occasionally took almost half an hour for a flight to completely settle on the ponds. Geese are monogamous but will remate if one partner is killed. Most courtship takes place on water, but for snow and Ross's geese, once down to the last two suitors, the female may lead them into flight before she makes a final decision.

The early-arriving ducks are drab looking, showing little color. As fall progresses into winter, the males begin to develop their colorful nuptial plumage. Mallards are usually in full color by early October, and pintails by late November. Courtship flights, coinciding with their finest plumage, are a joy to watch. The showy drakes follow and fly around a female until she chooses one for a mate. Pintail and wigeon flights are particularly noticeable because the species are so numerous. Their flights generally consist of four or five drakes, but it is not unusual to see nine or ten drakes courting a female.

Northern Pintail Flight

Pintails are the most numerous waterfowl species that migrate south along the Pacific Flyway. Although California has a high winter population, it has not been a significant nesting area in recent times. Annually, in my day, only about six pairs nested on Gray Lodge. From November to January, courtship flights were always a special sight. Several males pursued a single female, seeking her acceptance as a mate. Even after the birds landed back on a pond, the males swirled around the female, spreading their wings and showing off.

Ducks arrive in separate flights by species, but have tolerance for other species once they are on the ponds. Four or five species might intermingle on a pond. The dabblers prefer shallower ponds, where they feed, heads down, tails up, on aquatic plants, insects, snails, tadpoles, and other aquatic animals on the pond bottom. Diving ducks prefer deeper ponds where they dive for tubers, leaves and stems of aquatic plants, invertebrates, and insects. Geese tend to stay with their own kind on the ponds. Mixed-species groups of geese occasionally graze together or feed on seeds in the harvested rice fields.

Most ducks are paired before the northern migration begins. There have been reports of courtship flights at northern migration and breeding areas, possibly because a hen has lost her mate and needs another drake to attempt to renest. The hen leads her chosen mate back to where she was raised or where she nested the previous year. Since ducks are not monogamous, a drake spends only a few weeks with a hen until she begins incubating her eggs. Subsequent breeding (renesting or nesting the following year) is usually done with a different hen, often in a completely different breeding area.

The showy wood duck is not a migrant but a resident bird whose numbers have dramatically increased with the advent of the California Wood Duck Program in 1991. The male wood duck, with its crest and bright colors, is a spectacular sight. From 1940 to 1942, while a student at Chico State College, I often hunted along Butte Creek, south of Chico.

A JEWEL IN THE PACIFIC FLYWAY

Also, as a biology major, I was required to make many Butte Creek field trips and studies. While hiking along the creek, I always saw an abundance of wood ducks as they flushed in and out of the trees. During a pheasant research project in 1946, I again frequented the habitats along Butte Creek. The wood ducks were still there, though in slightly diminished numbers. Back then, the creek was a beautiful stream that meandered through farmlands south of Chico into the Butte Sink on the west and northwest sides of the Sutter Buttes. Many years before, as agriculture first developed in the area, levees had been built along the creek, far enough back from the stream to allow for the winter overflow. In the rich riparian habitat between the creek banks and the levees, trees such as cottonwoods, willows, oaks, black walnuts, ashes, and sycamores thrived alongside the usual riparian vines and shrubs: wild grape, blackberry, elderberry, and poison oak.

After I was transferred to Gray Lodge, I was so involved with refuge operations that I did not get back up Butte Creek for a few years. When I did, sometime in the 1960s, a friend took me for a flight over the valley in his light plane. I was shocked to see that Butte Creek had been almost entirely denuded of natural habitat. The land between the creek banks and the levees had been cleared and planted in agricultural crops. The creek looked like a channelized man-made ditch, as much of it does today. My first thought was, "What happened to the wood ducks?" To my knowledge, no studies were made to determine where they went. Some probably moved eastward to Honcut Creek, which runs into the Feather River and still had

Wood Ducks

The male wood duck (left) is generally recognized as one of the most beautiful of waterfowl. The increase in the population of these native nesting birds is heartwarming and is due in part to the installation of man-made nest boxes that supplement the supply of natural tree cavities.

considerable natural habitat. Other wood ducks may have moved south into the Butte Sink. But loss of habitat usually leads to lower wildlife numbers, and Butte Creek had temporarily lost its wood ducks. The good news is that Butte Creek runs along one border of the Upper Butte Basin Wildlife Area, where much riparian habitat is being restored along the waterway.

I saw only an occasional wood duck on Gray Lodge for many years, as the refuge had only marginal habitat for them. Grazing cattle had cropped off tree shoots, so the original refuge had very few trees. This was also true of the pastures and farmlands that were purchased to enlarge Gray Lodge. As vegetation began to grow along the ditches and ponds as part of the habitat development plan, I saw a few more wood ducks. By then, it was well known that wood ducks, which nest in tree cavities, will readily use man-made structures for nesting. As time allowed, the refuge staff and I put up a few boxes, which had low to moderate use. Since then, it has been learned that maintaining a successful population of nesting wood ducks does not end with nailing boxes to trees. Since 1990, numerous wood duck nesting projects have been established in the Central Valley with

Channelized Butte Creek

Flowing out of the mountains, Butte Creek passes through the canyons below Paradise, along the south edge of Chico, and across the upper Sacramento Valley into the Butte Sink on the west side of the Sutter Buttes. Historically, there was extensive flooding in the area south of Chico every winter. Early in the 1900s, as agriculture developed, levees were built along the creek from Chico to the sink, seen at left as two white strips, which are roads atop the levees. Through the 1940s, the overflow area between the levees and the creek was heavily wooded riparian habitat, home to lots of wildlife, particularly wood ducks (below). Reclamation work begun in the 1950s drastically changed the creek.

Native Elderberry

The elderberry thrives wherever riparian habitat is maintained. The bushes are found scattered around Gray Lodge. As I came upon this bush (above left), I discovered six or seven California quail. The berries (above right) appear in late summer and early fall, providing food for cedar waxwings, sparrows, and other birds.

the formation of the California Wood Duck Program, a network of more than a thousand volunteers that is supported by the California Waterfowl Association, the California Department of Fish and Game, and the University of California at Davis.

The value of this program is clearly supported by statistics from one of the most organized groups that volunteers at Gray Lodge. Thirty dedicated volunteers—ten crews of three each—install, service, clean, and monitor the boxes and record the nesting activities of the wood ducks. It is the largest single-area project in the state. For the past several years, approximately 370 nest boxes have been available for wood ducks at Gray Lodge. On average, 80 percent are occupied by wood ducks. Successful nests usually number near 300, producing two to three thousand ducklings annually. Other species using the wood duck boxes include barn owls, western screech owls, honey bees, starlings, ash-throated flycatchers, northern flickers, wrens, and opossums. In some years, several of the boxes are not used by any wildlife. Boxes in other areas of the Sacramento Valley are used by ringtails, bats, and squirrels as well. The wood duck program is an excellent example of Aldo Leopold's vision that man's helping hand can aid and preserve wildlife.

Many people think of the American coot as waterfowl, because its habitat and migration patterns are similar to those of ducks and geese. In managing the refuge, my staff and I treated them much the same. Coots are actually rails, belonging to the Rallidae family. They migrate to Gray Lodge in September and October and move north again about the first week of April. They are definitely nocturnal migrants. In all my years at Gray Lodge, I never saw a migrating flock arriving or leaving. But they did come in good numbers, ten thousand or more. Coots tend to flock close together. My family and the Gray Lodge staff commonly called them "dumb coots." They flew into power lines and were also a hazard as they bunched up and crossed roads, right into busy traffic, to move between water and fields. It was legal—and easy—to shoot coots during hunting season, but few hunters bothered. The "dumb coots" serve a purpose. They are an important part of the refuge's food web, as they are a main food source for red-tailed hawks and other raptors.

Two hundred to three hundred sandhill cranes usually arrive in October to spend the winter at Gray Lodge. They had been coming annually to the shallow ponds in the sanctuary area before I went to Gray Lodge, they came all the years I was there, and they still come to the area. I could hear their loud, distinctive calls before I saw the birds fly into a shallow pond, four to eight inches deep, in the sanctuary part of the refuge. During the day, the cranes fly out to forage. Sandhills eat rodents, insects, frogs, bulbs, berries, and agricultural grain. In the daytime, they use open fields, with a clear view in all directions. Just after sundown, they fly back to their ponds to roost for the night. Flights to northern nesting grounds in the western mountain valleys, the marshes of Canada, and the Yukon-Kuskokwim River Deltas of Alaska are in progress by March and early April.

Another magnificent waterbird sometimes seen at Gray Lodge is the American white pelican, easily recognized by its great size, long, heavy yellow bill, and big throat pouch. Although pelicans look awkward and

Nesting Coot

Although coots are primarily migratory birds, eight to ten pairs nest on Gray Lodge each spring. They build big, bulky nests out in open, stable waters. Some are anchored; some are floating. It is not uncommon to count fourteen to sixteen eggs in a nest. Young coots look like little cuddly, black balls with red beaks. But take care—they can scratch and peck ferociously, just like their parents.

cumbersome when resting on or taking off from the water, they are beautiful and graceful in flight. They fly synchronized in a line, following a leader, flapping a few times, then sailing, flapping and sailing, on and on, in a slow, easy manner. White pelicans once nested in many parts of California, but now nest primarily in the Salton Sea, in the Klamath Basin, and at several lakes in eastern Oregon. The nonbreeding pelicans are the birds seen at Gray Lodge during the spring and summer.

PARTICULARLY FROM THE 1920S FORWARD, the development of agriculture and reclamation water districts resulted in great loss of habitat for marshland wildlife in the Sacramento Valley. The appropriation of wetlands for other uses affects all the wildlife that frequents these areas. Wrens and rails, for instance, require heavy tule-cattail vegetation. Mudflats and extremely shallow water are the necessary feeding beds for avocets, stilts, sandpipers, dunlins, and yellowlegs. Shallow ponds provide food for bitterns, herons, and egrets. The tall trees of riparian habitat and forested wetlands serve as nesting rookeries for herons and egrets.

Virginia Rail and Nest
(ABOVE)
You can readily identify this rail by the slightly decurved, reddish bill and the rusty body coloration. The bird is about the size of a meadowlark. Even though rails inhabit Gray Lodge, they are very secretive and rarely seen, remaining hidden in the heavy marsh cover. Rail nests are especially well hidden. Even though I saw the adults and knew the nests should be there, I never found one until shortly before I retired. I saw the hen fly up and I searched for ten minutes before I found this nest.

The Elusive Sora (RIGHT)
Although this is reportedly the most common rail in California, it is still not very common at Gray Lodge. Soras are often difficult to observe, as they prefer the dense cover of tules, cattails, and sedges. They eat the seeds of marsh plants and also consume duckweeds and aquatic insects. Loss of permanent pond habitat has contributed to the decline of the sora population.

Sandhill Cranes

Traveling in great flocks, sandhill cranes fly with slow, steady strokes, their long necks outstretched (left). They have a very distinct call that carries two miles or so. I knew they were coming before I could see them flying into Gray Lodge. As they move around their favorite pond on the refuge, the cranes exhibit a stately grace. A memorable sight in late winter and early spring is their mating dance. The ritual starts with a deep bow, followed by hops, leaps, skips, turns, and more bows, all with wings spread, picking up speed at each stage.

The original Gray Lodge refuge had about five alkali ponds. Another dozen came with the small ranches acquired when the refuge was enlarged. The alkaline conditions prevented plants from growing, so the shallow ponds remained open, and their borders were broad and clear. This was ideal for shorebirds, which probed the mudflats of the ponds for food and used the upper borders for nesting. At Gray Lodge, American avocets and black-necked stilts came and went year-round, and at least fifteen pairs of each species nested on the refuge each year. Migrant sandpipers, dowitchers, curlews, yellowlegs, dunlins, and other occasional shorebirds also used the ponds in fall, winter, and spring. The resident killdeer foraged along wetland borders.

It took me a while to realize that the alkali ponds were disappearing and why. As intensive water developments accelerated, movement of fresh water through the ponds leached the salts out of the soil, the ponds deepened, and vegetation developed. My staff and I had no choice but to carry out our plans, as our primary goal was to create healthy marshland habitat, and movement of fresh water throughout the area was crucial. Agricultural development was causing the same changes throughout the Sacramento Valley, resulting in a significant waning of shorebird populations.

Great blue herons, great egrets, and snowy egrets adapted fairly well to feeding in the rice fields and were readily observed when I first came to live in Chico in the early 1940s. The birds congregate in rookeries and nest only in the upper reaches of trees. Several major rookeries of these species were still scattered throughout the area from Chico to Butte Sink until a serious pest, the big rice leaf-miner, infested rice fields in 1956. Extensive use of the insecticide dieldrin to control this pest had a widespread effect on wildlife and greatly reduced the populations of wading birds through loss of their food base and secondary poisoning from pesticide accumulation in their remaining foods.

The population of herons and egrets in the historical Huffman rookery, west of Gridley, was considerably reduced that year. This rookery received its final blow in 1957, when all the trees were removed, and the area was drained and leveled for rice production. As rookeries disappeared in the valley, it was my hope that Gray Lodge's developing forested wetlands would become the site of future rookeries. Herons and egrets had always fed at Gray Lodge. I was unable to determine which birds were migrants and which birds were from local rookeries, but I never observed any nesting on the area before 1957. I wasn't sure where the great blue herons and great egrets from the Huffman rookery had relocated and presumed that they had moved into the Butte Sink west of Gray Lodge, where other active rookeries still existed.

American White Pelicans
Pelicans came to Gray Lodge intermittently all year. I saw more of the birds in the spring and summer when some of the ponds were low and they came to forage for carp and other fish. Sitting on the shallow water, the pelicans made quick, effective jabs for the fish. They were also seen along the ditch banks, preening and grooming. In flight, they are majestic.

American Bittern
Hikers often walk right past these birds (far left) without seeing them. Bitterns can stand rigid with their head and bill pointed skyward (below). Along with their brown-and-tan coloration, they blend perfectly with the vegetation. Even newly hatched young (above) point their heads upward in the typical pose of adult bitterns. The nests are in very heavy weed cover, not far from a ditch or pond. Frogs, tadpoles, and beetles and other insects are the major diet of these birds on Gray Lodge. I once watched an adult bittern stalk a bullfrog and catch it on the first try. One of the most interesting sounds heard in a springtime marsh is that of the male American bittern. Some writers have described it as the sound of a gurgling hand pump.

I do think, however, that the loss of the Huffman rookery was responsible for the first nesting rookery for snowy egrets and black-crowned night-herons on Gray Lodge. A colony of these wading birds, which nest in tule swales or trees, established a rookery in the tules and cattails surrounding an alkali pond on the former Watson Ranch area of Gray Lodge in 1957. We kept a close protective surveillance and maintained adequate water in the refuge ponds for foraging. This proved beneficial, as the number of birds gradually increased. In 1971, fourteen years later, this rookery was abandoned, apparently due to predation of young by a pair of ospreys nesting in the Sutter Buttes. Since that time, rookeries in both tule swales and tall trees have been established and abandoned in various locations on the area.

In the 1970s, a colony of great blue herons moved into a grove of trees on the north side of Rising River. Within a year, they were joined by great egrets. Then, a few years later, snowy egrets and black-crowned night-herons moved into the lower branches of shorter trees in the grove to form

a four-species rookery. Sometime in the 1980s, the birds abandoned the rookery. The good news is that there is now a well-established four-species rookery in the sanctuary area. Another is becoming established on nearby Rising River. Herons and egrets are very sensitive to human intrusion or unusual noises and readily abandon an area. Control of public use and sensitive management practices during the nesting season are essential to preserving rookeries.

The most successful introduction of a game bird in California has been the ring-necked pheasant. The first introduction of pheasants into California was in 1857, but few birds survived. Large-scale productive introduction in Oregon occurred in the 1880s. In 1889, the California State Board of Fish and Game Commissioners obtained 140 wild-trapped pheasants from Oregon and released them in various locations in the central part of the state. From this first successful introduction and other small plantings, the ring-neck began to establish self-sustaining populations in several locations, but the species had the most reproductive success in the Sacramento Valley. By 1916, seven to eight thousand pheasants were in California, and thereafter,

Killdeer and Nest (TOP)
Gravel beds along roadways and parking lots were the most common killdeer nesting locations on Gray Lodge. The birds typically made a little cup in the gravel and laid four speckled eggs. Unfortunately, roadways and parking lots sometimes needed grading and mowing. Many nests were saved before work began, but the eggs looked so much like gravel that some were missed. Fortunately, killdeer readily renest and also have several broods a season.

The Good Actor (CENTER)
This killdeer is performing its characteristic broken wing act to lead the intruder away from the nest or young. Sometimes I followed briefly just to show my appreciation for the effectiveness of the performance.

American Avocet (BOTTOM)
When in full breeding plumage, avocets are beautiful birds. Even when their rusty heads and necks have faded to a grayish white, they are graceful to watch in flight or as they probe mudflats or shallow ponds. The avocet population on Gray Lodge has declined, but some birds still nest on the area, and incidentals are seen throughout the year.

the number kept increasing. In 1925, the first pheasant hunting season was held in the Owens Valley, primarily to reduce agricultural crop depredations. The first statewide hunting season was held in 1933, and there has been a pheasant hunting season every year since then.

Gray Lodge has usually maintained the highest pheasant numbers of all the wildlife areas in the Sacramento Valley. The pheasant may be the best researched bird in the state. From the early 1950s to the mid-1970s, the Pheasant Research Project was headquartered at Gray Lodge. Among other topics, studies focused on food habits, nesting, predation, population, diseases, and hunting effects. By 1980, researchers, as well as hunters, realized that the pheasant population was declining. Of the several factors responsible, the major one was the loss of habitat as intensive, efficient,

Rookery Hierarchies

In the early 1970s, great blue herons started a rookery in a grove of tall trees on the north Rising River area of Gray Lodge (below left). In subsequent years, snowy egrets and black-crowned night-herons nested in the lower trees of the grove. Then, great egrets (left) moved in just below the great blue herons in the same tree. For a few years, Gray Lodge had a four-species rookery, a real treasure. There seems to be a pecking order for the location of nests in rookeries with multiple species. Great egret nests are situated in the upper branches in groves of oak, cottonwood, and eucalyptus trees. If snowy egrets are nesting in the same rookery, their nests are on a lower level than those of great egrets; if night-herons are present, their nests are even lower.

Snowy Egret Nestling (BELOW RIGHT)

Standing in the nest, this nestling was seemingly wondering what to do next. I went away after quickly taking two pictures. The nest was in a clump of tules in a pond thirty inches deep, one of several dozen nests within a rookery in a permanent pond area. The nestling was old enough to make several pecking attempts to let me know I was unwelcome.

Dry Marsh

This marsh where a snowy egret and black-crowned night-heron rookery existed had been dried up for vegetation control, one of the tough decisions that must be made in managing a wildlife area. The tule nests were vulnerable to foxes, raccoons, and other predators. The rookery was abandoned before the area was cleared and reflooded.

Black-crowned Night-herons

Night-herons and snowy egrets share nesting areas. They are compatible possibly because egrets forage by day and night-herons forage at night. The nestling at far right is exhibiting a typical reaction to an intruder: standing up, mouth agape, and lunging toward the unwelcome visitor. After a couple of weeks, nestlings lose this bravado and climb down into the tule clumps when alarmed.

large-scale farming escalated throughout the Central Valley. Pheasants are not very venturesome birds. They rarely move more than one mile from where they were hatched. All their needs—food, cover, water, and space—are usually met within that area. With increasing agricultural efficiency, much of the good pheasant protective cover between small crop fields and along ditch banks was leveled to provide more crop acreage and to create turn-around areas for large farming equipment. Use of pesticides and fertilizers has undoubtedly taken a toll on the pheasant population. Another big factor in the decline has been the influx of new predators. Traditional predators—raccoons, skunks, gopher snakes, gray foxes, crows, hawks, and owls—were joined by opossums, red foxes, Norway rats, and feral house cats, as well as the returning coyote.

I have had a special interest in birds of the Columbidae family (doves and pigeons) since I raised pigeons as a boy. When I became manager at Gray Lodge, it was time for me to do a research project and thesis to complete the requirements for a master's degree. Dr. A. Starker Leopold, my

Choice Pheasant Nesting Habitat

This field (above), with its mixture of oats, vetch, and other plants, always had the greatest density of pheasant nests. You have to look carefully to see a hen pheasant (above left inset), as the nest is hidden in cover that blends with the hen's body colors. Note how well the chicks (left) also blend with their surroundings. A critical time is when the hen leads them from the nest. Using special calls and signals, she teaches them how to avoid predators and find food, water, and cover.

Pheasant Dump Nest (BOTTOM LEFT)

This is a nest where two or more hens have deposited eggs, a total of twenty-nine. Note that the nest does not contain down or other material. Dump nests are often seen early in the nesting season. According to one theory, hens may lay eggs in dump nests before they are ready to build their own nests and brood their own eggs.

Cock Pheasant Vanity

Ring-necked pheasant roosters are beautiful birds. It is truly special to see a rooster in full plumage, crowing up on a levee or a rice check. Pheasants were part of my everyday experience as they strutted around, protecting their territories. The proud, pugnacious cock pheasants seemed to disappear during August and early September, when they lost most of their color and looked scraggly for a few weeks. I decided maybe it was vanity that kept them hidden during this unbecoming phase.

master's thesis chairman, suggested that I study the life history and productivity of a population of western mourning doves. For three years, I followed a colony of doves nesting at Willow Pond in the southeast area of the original refuge. The findings of my research showed, in part, that they nested in trees. I saw only two ground nests in my thirty-two years at Gray Lodge. The nesting period extended from mid-March to as late as the third week in September, when the last squabs left the nest. Ninety-six percent of the mourning dove nests in the three-year study had clutches of two eggs, and pairs nested an average of five times per year. Productivity per pair per season averaged 6.3 squabs, up to departure from the nest. One season, a nest was used six times by one pair; all nestings were successful, with all 12 young fledged.

My productivity records confirmed that the mourning dove population was stable, and the species could safely remain on the list of game birds. In the early 1960s, however, there was a movement in the U.S. Congress to protect them, as doves came under the federal Migratory Bird Treaty Act. The California State Assembly sent a resolution to Congress requesting that the dove remain a game bird. These statistics were cited: estimated population statewide on September 1, opening day of dove hunting season, was 18 million birds, of which 6 million could be safely harvested although only 2 million were actually taken. At the time, doves were the quarry of almost two hundred thousand hunters annually. The federal legislation to end dove hunting was unsuccessful, and the dove remains one of the most popular game birds in California.

SEVERAL SPECIES OF BIRDS OF PREY are year-round residents of Gray Lodge Wildlife Area. Most numerous is the red-tailed hawk, which hunts in both marshes and dry fields, taking small mammals, small birds, reptiles, and amphibians. Red-tails also feast on coots year-round and, in the winter, on waterfowl crippled by hunters. American kestrels are often seen on their favorite perching places—power lines and wire fences—from which they pounce on small birds, large insects, small mammals, and sometimes reptiles. White-tailed kites hover over fields with heavy weed cover as they look for voles. Northern harriers fly low over marshes and occasionally dry fields in search of small mammals and birds, including ducklings. All of these hawks nest at Gray Lodge. Sharp-shinned, Cooper's, and red-shouldered hawks are seen intermittently throughout the year on Gray Lodge, but I never found their nests.

I knew that hawks moved down from the snow-covered high elevations in winter to forage in the Sacramento Valley, but I was surprised

Quail Habitat

The photograph below documents a success story because it shows a completely hatched quail nest. The population of California quail in the Sacramento Valley is under pressure as suitable habitat is disappearing, and the ground nests are vulnerable to an increasing number of predators. I have seen more quail on Gray Lodge than other parts of the valley. Perhaps this is partially due to the spread of the quailbush (bottom) and multiflora rose we planted years ago to ensure escape cover.

Blackbird Nest with Cowbird Egg

Brown-headed cowbirds have a sneaky strategy. Rather than build nests of their own, they lay their eggs in the nests of other birds—about thirty eggs per season, depositing one or two in each host nest. Here, a light-colored cowbird egg stands out among the eggs of the red-winged blackbird host. The host birds incubate the eggs and feed the young until they leave the nest.

Mourning Dove Nests

Doves are good parents. The male brings nest materials to the female for assembling the nest. Both parents incubate the eggs and feed the young. However, their nest is a loose, flimsy platform of twigs made even more precarious by poor choice of location where wind and weather can take their toll. Three days after I took this photograph (above left), the nest was destroyed by wind. I wondered if doves would use a man-made nest structure, as many birds do. After some experimentation, I settled on wire hardware cloth as the best choice of material (above right). Wire cone nests were installed on Gray Lodge, and their use has spread to other states (see page 150).

by how much the hawk population at Gray Lodge increased from December into February. Raptor studies done later on the area confirmed that the hawk population increased 100 percent from fall through winter. Red-tailed hawks showed the greatest increase, probably due to Gray Lodge's ample food base, especially the abundant coots.

I usually spotted two or three golden eagles each year. After the Oroville Dam Afterbay ponds were developed in 1968, I began to see two or three bald eagles a year. During my first five years at Gray Lodge, I observed at least one peregrine falcon each year. After that, I saw one only every two or three years until my last sighting in 1976. Like the herons and egrets, they were vulnerable to pesticides.

White-tailed Kite Nest

This nest was located in the upper branches of an old prune tree in an orchard acquired with the Cassady Ranch addition to Gray Lodge. The last of three juveniles was still in the nest; the others had flown off but were not far away. I had watched the female forage from the nest, going up to three-quarters of a mile. Kites like open fields rich with voles, mice, and gophers. They often hover forty feet above the ground as they search for prey.

Turkey vultures eat almost exclusively carrion. An amazing sense of smell, more than sight, leads them to food. Road-killed animals are one food source. But I always wondered if the quantity of roadkills, along with field kills, was enough to support the number of birds I saw. No longer do vultures eat dead cattle, which farmers load up and take to a tallow plant. The only concentrated feeding of turkey vultures that I observed on Gray Lodge was when my staff and I drained a pond or ditch and the birds came to gorge on the dead carp. A group of about thirty-five vultures habitually roosts in a grove of tall cottonwood trees in the sanctuary area, but vultures have never nested on Gray Lodge. They nest in the nearby Sutter Buttes.

Barn owls, probably the most easily recognized owls because of their characteristic white heart-shaped faces, certainly are aptly named. With

Consummate Hunter

I generally saw the fast, medium-sized Cooper's hawk during the fall and winter months. There was no record that they nested on the area. Their diet consists primarily of small birds — including sparrows, meadowlarks, quail, and doves, which they generally capture on the wing. I once watched a Cooper's hawk kill a cock pheasant, but this was probably not a common occurrence.

Most male and female hawks have similar coloration. This is not so with the harrier. The male is light gray, with black wing tips; the female is mottled brown. Both have a visible white rump. When hunting, they fly low over marsh areas, as their former name, marsh hawk, indicates. Harrier nests are located on the ground and are conspicuous despite the surrounding heavy cover. The female is sometimes seen nearby on a lookout perch, as in this photograph.

the enlargements of Gray Lodge in the 1950s through the 1970s, the refuge acquired eight barns. Barn owls were nesting in all of them, as well as in an abandoned clubhouse on the original property. Three of these barns are still standing, and barn owls still nest there, forty-plus years later. Gray Lodge is a good feeding place for the owls, which eat a wide range of small animals, especially gophers, mice, ground squirrels, Norway and black rats, and blackbirds. They also like amphibians, crustaceans, and other creatures that inhabit the marshes.

At least four pairs of great horned owls nest on Gray Lodge each year. They perch in tall trees, from which they spot and hunt prey. It is easy to determine the species' eating habits by collecting and examining the pellets they regurgitate. Main food sources at Gray Lodge are cottontail rabbits,

Turkey Vulture

Vultures are both resident and migratory in California. When I was at Gray Lodge, a colony of about thirty-five birds roosted, their wings spread open, in a grove of tall cottonwood trees in the sanctuary area, which was also a great blue heron rookery. One of their nesting areas in the Sacramento Valley is in the ledges and cliffs of the higher peaks of the Sutter Buttes.

Burrowing Owl
This owl was photographed at the entrance to its burrow, which two years earlier had belonged to ground squirrels. Burrowing owls seldom make their own burrows, preferring to take over abandoned ones. As habitat developments progressed on Gray Lodge, fewer burrowing owls were seen, as areas suitable for the owls became marshland.

jackrabbits, ground squirrels, Norway and black rats, muskrats, and California voles, also known as meadow mice. An intensive study would likely identify many more prey items. A pair of great horned owls resides in the town of Gridley and uses a huge valley oak in our front yard as a perching site. My wife and I enjoy the sound of their *whooos* in the night. Except for part of a cottontail rabbit leg a few years ago, the pellets found in our yard have contained exclusively Norway rats. We doubly appreciate the pair for cleaning out the rat infestation in our dense ivy.

When I came to Gray Lodge in 1947, the spectacular wintering waterfowl population had already arrived in the Sacramento Valley, and the refuge was teeming with birds. Hearing the geese calling in the night, I was unable to sleep for the first week. I did not mind—their calls were music to my ears. In the decades after that first week until I left in 1980, it was a joy to observe and photograph the hundreds of other resident and migratory birds on the refuge. To this day, I still find immense pleasure in watching and recording the valley's bird life, and I still feel that the sound of geese calling is music to my ears.

Great Horned Owl

This formidable hunter has powerful talons and a sharp hooked bill. Despite its size, it seems more silent on the wing than other owls. For the sake of the rodent, rabbit, raccoon, barn owl, nesting duck, heron, and egret populations at Gray Lodge, it was probably a good thing that only four pairs of great horned owls resided there when I was manager.

Short-eared Owl

Intermittent winter migrants and occasional nesters at Gray Lodge, short-eared owls can sometimes be seen resting during the day near the tops of thick tule clumps along the visitor's route. They are night feeders, preying on mice and other small mammals. They also eat snakes and amphibians, even some of the numerous blackbirds.

CHAPTER 5

Deer to Otters to Crayfish

Visitors to Gray Lodge at peak times are accustomed to seeing large numbers of wintering and resident birds. Most, however, are unaware of the abundance of other wildlife species that inhabit the refuge, from large mammals such as black-tailed deer and coyotes to voles, gophers, and a host of aquatic creatures. More species are nocturnal than not. Many mammals, especially small ones, cannot readily be identified in the wild—it is often necessary to have the animal "in hand" to make a positive identification. Over the years I spent at Gray Lodge, I watched some species come, others wane, and still others go. Some were welcome, others not so welcome.

Mammals and other wildlife are more likely to be observed in the spring or fall than in the hot summer or cold, damp winter. Young of the year may be seen occasionally in the summer, while being trained by their mother or having escaped their mother's eye. But time of day is more important than time of year for spotting wildlife. Most mammals are hidden away in dens, burrows, and thickets in the middle of the day. They are more likely to be out in the early-morning or evening hours. Most apt to be seen at these times are deer, opossums, skunks, beavers, ringtails, foxes, ground squirrels, and possibly river otters or muskrats. Visitors can

Deer at Sunset (OPPOSITE)
This is a favorite picture. I stopped to observe the marsh, took some photographs, and then sat and enjoyed the sunset. As I was starting to leave, two deer crossed the pond, giving me this special view.

Tiger Swallowtail (ABOVE)
An added bonus of a Gray Lodge visit is the chance to see small creatures such as butterflies and dragonflies.

Ringtail

This relative of the raccoon, only slightly larger than a ground squirrel, had been seen in the Butte Sink area before the species showed up on Gray Lodge for the first time in 1970. Ringtails originally inhabited nearby mountain slopes and foothills but then moved down into the valleys. Ringtails are decidedly nocturnal. Small rodents are among their favorite foods. They also climb trees to eat birds and bird eggs. Great horned owls, foxes, and coyotes are their main enemies.

increase their chances of seeing wildlife by doing their homework, especially by learning what species are found on the refuge and which habitats they prefer. Serious nature observers should hike the trails alone, as quietly as possible. It is best for large groups to break up into smaller groups before exploring the refuge.

Visitors will not have much difficulty spotting black-tailed deer, the largest mammals on Gray Lodge and the most likely to be seen and recognized year-round. It was a happy day when the first deer were spotted on Gray Lodge in 1964. By 1980, a resident herd had developed and was large enough that hunting—an archery hunt—was permitted for the first time on the area.

Hikers may also see jackrabbits and cottontail rabbits. The black-tailed jackrabbit is not a true rabbit, but a hare. A hare does not build a nest. Instead, it bears its young in an open grass- or weed-covered field. The young are highly precocial, born fully furred and with eyes open and able to hop around. The jackrabbit is found throughout California except in the high mountains. One of Dr. A. Starker Leopold's students, Bob Lechleitner, did his doctoral research on the jackrabbit on Gray Lodge from fall of 1954 through spring of 1956. He found that they have rather well-defined home ranges of thirty to fifty acres. The density of the population was one jackrabbit per acre, which results in a considerable overlap of home ranges. Lechleitner documented pregnant females during every month of the year. Numbers were especially high from January to April. Young were capable of breeding at approximately eight months of age. No wonder they are abundant and widespread.

A JEWEL IN THE PACIFIC FLYWAY

Young Fawn

One day I happened on a doe and her fawn moving away from me. As they went through a small patch of heavy cover, the fawn disappeared as the doe went on through. That told me where to find the fawn. I quickly took pictures and left so the mother could return. If you think you have found an abandoned fawn, you most likely have not. The mother knows where it is and will be back soon to nurse it.

Nevada Cypress
(ABOVE)

These well-browsed trees are evidence that Gray Lodge deer found them good eating. More than one hundred of the trees were planted on the area.

Hiding Jackrabbit

This black-tailed jackrabbit is dead still and better hidden than the photograph indicates. Its drab coloration provides good camouflage. Jackrabbits also run to escape their enemies, but coyotes, golden eagles, barn owls, red-tailed hawks, great horned owls, and foxes are also swift.

Albino Deer

An albino strain of the black-tailed deer has existed in the area from Chico south to the Sutter Buttes for many generations. Years ago, I interviewed a man who had personal knowledge of sightings prior to World War I. An albino was born on Gray Lodge in 1968, and at least three more were known to have been born there since then. One, sometimes more, are seen each year in nearby areas.

During my first several years at Gray Lodge, a dozen or more jack-rabbits regularly ran down the road ahead of my car as I drove the short distance home from the refuge entrance. Today, they are still present but in somewhat reduced numbers. This is most likely due to the increase in numbers and species of predators. Coyotes, foxes, hawks, and great horned owls prey on both young and adult jackrabbits. Snakes prey on the young.

Desert cottontails, which are true rabbits, feed on grass and other herbaceous plants but do not stray far from heavy thickets or shrubbery where they hide from predators. To protect and enhance the cottontail population at Gray Lodge, we let wild blackberry bushes grow and planted quailbush. Back in these thickets and shrubs, a female makes a nest in a shallow hole or a burrow and lines it with her own fur. The young, born blind, naked, and helpless, stay in the nest and are fed by the mother until they are fully furred and able to care for themselves. Most people, as did I, like watching cottontails. Whereas a group of jackrabbits in a field acts like a bunch of loners, cottontails romp around together as if playing. They, too, have many predators, including snakes, hawks, owls, feral house cats, foxes, and coyotes.

Striped skunks are very active at night but may occasionally be out and about in the morning or evening, more likely on overcast days. These omnivorous mammals eat berries, beetles, grubs, grasshoppers, small snakes, and voles and other small mammals. Especially fond of bird eggs, they are a significant predator on the nests of ground-nesting birds.

It is always advisable to give skunks the right of way. I can state, from several encounters, that skunks have utmost confidence in their self-propelled defense system and do not hesitate to use it. I had one encounter that seemed to end in mutual respect. I was standing on a mound next to a tree, installing a wire cone dove nest. I felt something on my lower leg and thought a small limb had fallen. I didn't look down and kept working. Then, it happened again. I looked down and saw an adult skunk, standing upright, with its front feet against my leg. I automatically said "go away," and, surprisingly, it did, into nearby cover. I looked around and saw that the entrance to the den was on the side of the mound. The skunk was just telling me that I was intruding in its domain. I went away so the skunk could return home. Would that all my encounters had ended as well.

Destroyed Cinnamon Teal Nest
A close look told me that this was not a hatched nest. The shells had been licked clean—the typical nest destruction method of a skunk. The skunk cracks an egg with its teeth, then sticks its snout into the egg and licks it clean. In contrast, a raccoon is messier and scatters broken eggshells about.

Striped Skunk in Defensive Stance
Through the years, I had many interesting encounters with skunks. I did not always come out the winner. Clothing could be washed, and I could take a shower, but it took a long time for skunk odor to fade from camera cases and gear.

The beaver is the largest rodent native to the North American continent. One beaver at Gray Lodge weighed in at seventy pounds. Beavers were largely responsible for the development of the American West. The first non-natives to spend significant time inland were trappers from the East seeking the highly valued beaver pelts. Their success brought other trappers. When they returned home, their tales of the lush valleys and rivers and abundant game brought overland settlers, even before the gold rush. By the 1900s, beavers had been trapped almost to extinction. In 1911, laws were passed to limit trapping seasons and take. Various successful conservation methods, such as live trapping and relocating, were carried out in the late 1930s and 1940s by the California Division of Fish and Game to reestablish the population. In the past, the beaver's major predator was man. This is no longer true. The market for beaver fur is small, and trapping and control methods are limited by law.

In some areas, I think that the beaver's comeback has been too successful. A small colony of beavers existed for many years in the Butte Sink, but none were found on Gray Lodge until the late 1960s. By 1980, the beaver population was thirty-five to forty individuals. By 2000, it had grown to approximately three hundred. Along with the increase in numbers

Beaver

Once hunted to near extinction, beavers have made an extraordinary comeback. They are industrious—building impressive lodges up to four feet tall—but their handiwork can damage refuge water control structures, affecting the habitat used by other wildlife.

has come a significant management problem. Beavers dam up irrigation control structures because they prefer water much deeper than the level desired by management for waterfowl. Some burrow into ditch banks to build their dens. Others construct three-to-four-foot-tall lodges of mud and limbs along the canals, which they enter underwater to reach their den in the upper dry part. To build their dams and lodges, beavers cut down willows, cottonwoods, and other trees and shrubs. Strictly plant eaters, they feed on tules, cattails, leaves, and grasses, as well as various limbs, twigs, and bark. At night, they are very busy with their building and feeding activities. During the day, they sleep in their dens.

The beaver problems on Gray Lodge will undoubtedly accelerate. The only potential predator—though not a very effective one in my opinion—is the coyote, which is not yet present on the refuge in sufficient numbers to help control the beaver population. This may sound as if I don't like beavers. On the contrary, I was delighted when they moved into Gray Lodge. But little did I know how rapidly their numbers would increase as riparian habitat developed. I respect beavers. Their ingenuity is amazing, their family fidelity admirable, their coats beautiful. I certainly don't advocate near extinction again, just beaver population control so Gray Lodge can be more effectively managed for all wildlife.

The most numerous mammal on Gray Lodge is probably the California vole, also called the meadow mouse, a species with wide distribution throughout the Central Valley. For his master's thesis, Michael Smith conducted a study of small mammals on the original Gray Lodge area in

1974. He selected three plots just under two and a half acres each and divided each plot into grids measuring about thirty-three feet square. Within each plot, he placed one hundred live traps. When a small mammal sprung a trap, Smith clipped a claw, to avoid counting that animal again. Of the original trap captures, 114 were voles, 73 were feral house mice, and 42 were deer mice. Projecting these figures onto the total area of Gray Lodge confirmed that these small mammals were numerous enough to be significant in the local food cycle. Mice, rats, and gophers are foods for owls, hawks, foxes, coyotes, and snakes. Herons, egrets, bitterns, otters, and many other species take advantage of them when their numbers are high. The California vole breeds and raises young year-round, particularly when food is abundant. Litter size averages four to six. Gestation is twenty-one days, and young are weaned in about twenty-one days. The females reach maturity and can breed within twenty-nine days—hence their abundance in favorable habitat. The study also showed a significant population of the non-native feral house mouse.

Beechey Ground Squirrel

Historically, ground squirrels (right) were numerous throughout California except in arid deserts. Although their numbers lessened as agriculture increased in the Central Valley, they are still around. Their population decreased on Gray Lodge as pastures and grain fields were converted to ditches and ponds. Squirrels have to contend with some very efficient predators: red-tailed hawks and other large hawks, great horned owls, large gopher snakes, red and gray foxes, and coyotes. When I came upon this red-tailed hawk with a squirrel (bottom right), it flew away, leaving its prey. However, one animal's loss was another's gain: when I came back about ten minutes later, two turkey vultures were finishing the hawk's meal.

Another common small mammal on Gray Lodge is the valley pocket gopher, a rodent that is slightly larger than the vole. The population fluctuates in part due to management practices. Plowing fields for crops, for example, destroys gopher burrows, as does flooding the fields in fall. Nevertheless, these animals reproduce rapidly on an area such as Gray Lodge where year-round vegetative food is abundant. They may produce up to four litters per year, with each litter consisting of one to twelve young. Gophers on Gray Lodge do no harm and are significant in the diets of hawks, herons, owls, foxes, gopher snakes, and coyotes.

The muskrat, also abundant on Gray Lodge, is a small rodent easily recognized by its hairless, flattened tail and by its webbed hind feet. With these adaptations, the muskrat is very much at home in the water. It is not native to the west side of the Sierra Nevada but was brought into Northern California in the late 1920s for fur farms. Muskrats escaped from one such farm near Oroville and came down the Feather River during a flood in 1931. Eight years later, some were established on Gray Lodge. When I came in 1947, several lodges of tules and cattails, four to five feet high with a circumference of six to eight feet, could be seen on the sanctuary ponds. Muskrats continued to spread throughout Central California with the increase in irrigation and became a nuisance due to their burrowing in levees, dams, and rice checks. Private trapping provided some manner of control. At one time, muskrat fur, which is soft and thick, became the most important fur taken in California, both in the number of muskrats harvested and in the cash value of the pelts.

Valley Pocket Gopher

Gophers are seldom seen outside their burrow, but their presence can be detected by the mounds of earth at the entrance. This gopher had been flooded out of its burrow and was looking for high ground. The large front paws make gophers very efficient diggers. They dig their way through the soil in search of underground roots, tubers, and bulbs. Thus, they contribute to keeping the soil loose and moist, which helps provide healthy plants for other animals. The gopher itself is important in the food chain as it is preyed upon by several large birds and mammals as well as reptiles.

Muskrat and Lodge

Although not native to the Central Valley, the muskrat (above) is found throughout the area where ditches, ponds, and other water with some vegetation exist. The muskrat is nocturnal but sometimes feeds during the day. Occasionally it may be seen on Gray Lodge swimming between tule clumps and burrowing areas in ditch banks. The lodges (right) are a remarkable construction feat, especially for so small an animal. They rank right up there with beaver dams and lodges. Also like the beaver, the muskrat enters its home from under the water. In 1947, my first year at Gray Lodge, there were several large muskrat lodges on the ponds. After the rotating vegetation control program was begun, lodges were rarely seen on the area.

On Gray Lodge, muskrats became a definite problem as more levees, dams, and roads were developed. Beginning in the mid-1950s and continuing after I left in 1980, private trappers were hired to reduce the muskrat numbers. Annual takes ranged from eleven hundred to twenty-six hundred pelts. Despite this culling of the population, muskrat damage was an ever-present maintenance problem and had to be considered when new roads and levees were built. Since trapping in California has been greatly restricted except in rare instances, muskrat damage on wildlife areas and farms, particularly rice farms, will likely become a serious and expensive problem.

Unwelcome non-native animals on Gray Lodge include the prolific, aggressive, omnivorous Norway rat and its kin, the black rat. Black rats, found more often in fields than around buildings, are more likely than Norway rats to climb trees to reach bird nests. The Norway rat is bigger and heavier and preys on the young of the black rat. Black rats are omnivorous, feeding on grains, fruits, insects, mammals, and human garbage, and both rats are significant predators of ground-nesting birds, their eggs, and their young on wildlife areas. They are, in turn, prey for hawks, owls, foxes, and mink, but multiply faster than they are killed. Although these two rats are always too plentiful, their populations vary at times for unknown reasons. Some years, they are extremely abundant in the upper Sacramento Valley and can be seen scampering across country roads at night. The number of roadkills in those years is high.

With its black mask and ringed tail, the raccoon is readily recognizable. People tend to be sentimental about raccoons. Young ones are cute and easily tamed. Our children raised three newborns in different years. They were good house pets until they started getting up on kitchen counters and into the sink. Having learned the sound of the refrigerator door opening, they would come running and spill food everywhere before the door could be closed. By the time the animals were a year old or so, they became unpredictable

Raccoon

The presence of this nocturnal creature is most often evidenced by little handlike tracks left around the banks of ponds and ditches, where the raccoon has sought out crayfish, a favorite food item. Raccoons also consume bird eggs. The species is found throughout most of California, except desert areas. Greater numbers inhabit riparian and wetland habitat.

and would bite and scratch unexpectedly. Then they were moved to the "return" house, a former chicken coop beyond our backyard. The gate was left unlatched so the raccoons could come and go until they finally adapted to the outdoors and departed for good.

One year, when one of our raccoons was about four months old, a mountain-area game warden brought us a black bear cub whose mother had been killed by a truck. At first, the two animals were good playmates, tumbling, wrestling, and running around the house and yard. Against my wife's wishes, I did not trim the bear's claws as it enjoyed climbing the trees in our front yard. The bear grew fast and was soon bigger and stronger than the raccoon. In play, it almost tore an ear off the raccoon, and it bit the finger of one of our daughters. It was time for the bear to go, so I found a home for it at the children's petting area of the Fleishhacker Zoo in San Francisco.

Cute pets or not, raccoons are serious predators in wildlife areas. Greater numbers are found in riparian or wetland habitats than in other habitats. These omnivorous animals tend to eat whatever is handy or in season. They are active, covering lots of ground each night. Raccoons on Gray Lodge became a problem due to their predilection for bird eggs and, along with striped skunks, are major threats to the success of nesting pheasants and ducks.

Fortunately, soon after I went to Gray Lodge, the California Division of Fish and Game began a program for the purpose of lowering the populations of some predators in order to protect the populations of their prey. The program was aimed primarily at helping pheasants, waterfowl, and other ground-nesting birds. Just prior to nesting season, a state trapper was assigned to Gray Lodge for a six-week period. Target species were raccoons, skunks, opossums, Norway rats, black rats, and feral house cats. Prior pheasant research on the refuge had found a 42 percent rate of nest destruction. Nesting surveys after the first year of predator control showed a drop in the rate to 30 percent; the second year, to 14 percent.

The most unwelcome predator was the feral house cat. Most people have no concept of the number of house cats living and reproducing in the wild. Cats are efficient hunters, and their survival rate is high. By the third generation on Gray Lodge, these cats are big and fierce, resembling wild bobcats except for their long tails. Both tree- and ground-nesting birds have suffered from this especially significant predator as domestic cats have proliferated in the wild.

I probably enjoyed watching river otters more than any other mammals. Otters are primarily nocturnal, but a quiet, patient observer may see them in the daytime, particularly morning or evening. Although occasionally seen on land, they are almost continuously in water. Otters are very graceful as they swim through the canals. They are fun to watch as they play together in the water or take turns on the mud slides formed on canal banks. River otters like the abundant carp on Gray Lodge as well as amphibians, crayfish, and other aquatic life. They eat muskrats—thereby helping to control the population—and have been known to eat bird eggs, birds, ducklings, and small mammals. I saw little sign of that on Gray Lodge, probably because water was adequate year-round to supply the aquatic foods they prefer. Otters like to travel, so after new ditches were developed and connected, they used these waterways to move throughout the area. Their main predators historically were humans, who trapped otters for their fur and greatly reduced their

River Otter

Although otters are chiefly nocturnal, living at Gray Lodge for so many years allowed me many opportunities to see them during the day. I liked them not only because they are so graceful to watch but because they consume muskrats, which damage refuge levees.

Patrolling Coyotes

After I came to Gray Lodge, it was always a mystery that my staff and I did not see coyotes on the area when we knew they lived in the Sutter Buttes, just two miles away. They later moved into the area but never became as numerous as I expected them to be when I lived on the refuge. In the years since, they have spread throughout the Sacramento Valley, where they are seen patrolling rice checks and drain canals.

numbers. Populations have increased significantly since trapping of otters was banned in California in 1961.

Three members of the wild dog family, Canidae, inhabit Gray Lodge. The native gray fox was the only one on the refuge when I arrived. In 1961, the first red fox was reported on the area. In time, the more aggressive non-native red fox became dominant, and the gray fox became quite scarce. Since then, the population of gray foxes has increased, with red foxes still in evidence. The first sign of coyotes on the refuge was one caught in a trap in 1971. A coyote den was found on the area in the late 1970s, but up until I left, there was little indication that coyotes were increasing or even resident. Sometime in the 1980s, I visited with longtime hunters at the Gray Lodge check station who said that, for the first time, they were hearing coyotes howl at night. Their numbers have not increased nearly as much as I expected, however. Traditionally, the coyote has coexisted in other areas with either the red fox or the gray fox. On Gray Lodge, it seems to be coexisting with both.

Gray Fox

The gray fox is widely distributed throughout California except for Lassen and Modoc Counties. When I was at Gray Lodge, foxes dug their dens into levees and high mounds. The dens were so well hidden that they were hard to find. Locating a den was easier in the spring, when the young were in the den and pheasant remains were scattered nearby. Gray foxes eat other ground-nesting birds, as well as small mammals, grasshoppers, crickets, beetles, carrion, and some herbage, nuts, and fruit. By the time I left Gray Lodge, it was evident that the more aggressive non-native red fox was becoming more prevalent than the gray fox.

Since these canines are no longer trapped, they have no significant predators. The very young may be prey to great horned owls and an occasional visiting golden eagle. On Gray Lodge, adult coyotes and foxes destroy ground nests and kill hen pheasants and ducks. They also eat rabbits, mice, rats, gophers, and ground squirrels. Additional research on these canids will reveal more information about their impact on the area.

One surprise I had in the 1970s was finding a road-killed porcupine on a county road bordering Gray Lodge. I had thought that these animals never came out of the mountains or foothills. The literature told me that they are remarkable wanderers and can show up in unexpected areas, so I decided that this was a onetime occurrence. Several years later, I found another road-killed porcupine about a mile north of the Gray Lodge entrance. Since then, there have been a few reports of sightings of porcupines in trees in the town of Gridley. It will be interesting to see if these occurrences increase in the future.

Only one species of marsupial lives in the United States. This is the opossum. Opossums bear immature young whose development is completed in a pouch on the female's abdomen, just like the kangaroo. Native in various eastern states, opossums were brought to California in the early 1900s. They were first seen in the Los Angeles area, were recorded in San Jose by 1910, and were no doubt headed north, as the species adapts well to many environments. The first opossum recorded on Gray Lodge was

The lowland red fox was brought to the upper Sacramento Valley in the 1880s. This fast, aggressive species showed up on Gray Lodge in the 1960s. I came upon this fox as it was devouring a pheasant. Red foxes are particularly harmful to nesting ducks and pheasants. They are notorious for their habit of "caching" prey, including eggs, which results in the destruction of far more wildlife than what they eat.

trapped during animal control work in 1952. It was also the first recorded in Butte County. I was not overjoyed to see the opossum, as its reputation had preceded it. Today they are very much a part of California's valley and low-elevation fauna. These omnivorous animals are not popular on wildlife areas and will eat almost anything, including carrion. They especially like bird eggs, young birds, frogs, fish, and fruit. I once observed an opossum up a tree eating eggs from a mourning dove nest.

A WILDLIFE AREA HAS A WHOLE UNDERSTRUCTURE of smaller creatures. Most likely to be seen are bull-frogs. Wildlife watchers may spot an occasional snake, crayfish along banks, fish in ditches, and perhaps a turtle. The underwater world also has great variety: snails, mussels, aquatic insects, worms, leeches, fleas, fairy shrimp, amphibians, turtles, and the larvae of myriad invertebrate species. These creatures are all important parts of the food web. Drying up a part of the Gray Lodge marsh in summer is not detrimental to some water inhabitants; in fact, draining improves the value of the habitat for many wetland-dependent wildlife. For those inhabitants restricted to water, we tried to provide stable, permanent water on a portion of the refuge.

Opossum

The increase in the population of the non-native opossum in the Sacramento Valley is not good news. Opossums typically produce two litters a year, averaging seven young per litter. On wildlife areas, they readily eat the eggs of ground-nesting birds such as ducks, pheasants, meadowlarks, and quail. Their presence has aggravated the predation problems already caused by the native striped skunk and raccoon.

Carp are the most abundant fish in Gray Lodge waters, primarily because they are more adaptable. They can live in warm, murky, or shallow water. They can go into flooded fields where the water is less than two feet deep. Some wildlife conservationists do not like carp—they muddy the water, limit growth of aquatic plants, and cause other environmental problems. However, they also have significant value as food for other wildlife. Young carp are major diet items for raccoons, otters, garter snakes, bullfrogs, herons, pelicans, cormorants, and grebes, among others. They are the easiest fish to prey on because they feed in shallow water and are slow moving. Other fish in refuge waters, including black bass, channel catfish, and Sacramento perch, prefer the cool water of the deeper, wider ditches and pothole ponds.

When I first came to Gray Lodge, there were many bullfrogs, a few red-legged frogs, and an abundance of Pacific treefrogs. Within a few years, I no longer saw red-legged frogs, and I found few treefrogs. I assumed they had succumbed to predators such as the bullfrog or to pesticides in the water.

Channel Catfish

Early records indicate that the channel catfish was introduced into the San Joaquin River from the Mississippi Valley in 1874. In the upper Sacramento Valley, catfish were successfully planted in the lower Feather River in 1891. The species is now found in the Sacramento River, roughly south of Colusa, and the Feather River, south of where the Feather flows into the Sacramento and into the Sutter Bypass. The fish grow to a good size and have become a popular freshwater game fish in California. At Gray Lodge, they are mostly found in large ditches, particularly along the northwest boundary.

Mosquito Fish

These minnows, one and a half inches long, are remarkably efficient at eating mosquito larvae. An adult mosquito fish may eat one hundred to five hundred larvae per day. The female can reproduce three to six times per summer, with forty to more than sixty young each time. Beginning in the 1970s, in cooperation with the local mosquito abatement districts, a series of ponds was constructed on Gray Lodge for raising and holding mosquito fish for planting on the refuge and throughout nearby communities.

Western Toad (ABOVE)

When I came to Gray Lodge in 1947, western toads were not uncommon. By the mid-1950s, I realized they were no longer about. Between that time and when I retired in 1980, I did not see a single toad on the refuge. Their disappearance is still a mystery to me. Since part of the water supply came from agricultural drain ditches, I suspect that the toad population or their insect foods were decimated by pesticides in the water.

Western Pond Turtle (BELOW)

The western pond turtle lives in a variety of aquatic habitats throughout western California. The turtles have always been found on Gray Lodge but not in abundance. They like permanent or semipermanent ponds and ditches where they can loaf on logs, tule clumps, or mudflats. Anchoring old logs so they are partially submerged provides a basking spot from which turtles can slide into the water at any sign of trouble.

The bullfrog, the largest frog in California, is found throughout the state except in the high Sierra Nevada and the dry deserts. It is not native to the state but was introduced in the early 1900s. Bullfrogs rely on year-round ponds and ditches and do not survive well where vegetative cover is lacking. They have thrived because they prey on both vertebrates and invertebrates: fish, salamanders, smaller frogs, toads, snakes, ducklings, even mice.

The bullfrog is preyed upon by wading birds, garter snakes, river otters, minks, and raccoons. I once discovered a bullfrog captured by a western aquatic garter snake. The frog was making loud croaking sounds and puffing up its body, and the snake was finding the frog hard to swallow. A garter snake's needlelike teeth are slanted inward and therefore prey rarely escapes. But as I came closer to photograph the event, the snake started releasing its hold on the frog. This took about two minutes, then the snake slithered away. I examined the frog and, to my surprise, found no injuries. I let the frog go, and it bounded off. Having seen adult garter snakes swallow bullfrogs, I was startled when I examined the stomachs of some adult bullfrogs and found baby garter snakes, eight to ten inches long.

Bullfrog Tadpoles

Occasionally, for management purposes, ditches or ponds temporarily had to be dried up. Concentrations of tadpoles like the one here were sometimes left in the muddy bottoms. As time allowed, the tadpoles were scooped out and moved to fresh water. Those left behind were cleared out in a day or two by predators such as herons, egrets, and raccoons.

Crayfish are an interesting part of wetland ecology. Most crayfish in California are non-natives. The species that inhabits Gray Lodge waters is the hardy red swamp crayfish. Introduced into California in 1924, it is now the most widespread of the six species found in the state. It is very important in the life cycle of a marsh. Crayfish prey on snails, worms, insects, and small fish. They also eat their own kind. In turn, crayfish are eaten by many kinds of birds, fish, and mammals.

Found in a great variety of habitats, gopher snakes are the most abundant snake in California and the snake most often seen on Gray Lodge. These snakes enter the burrows of small mammals to capture prey. They are significant predators on the eggs and nestlings of ground-nesting birds. The snake population is thinned out by some mammals, hawks, owls, and other snakes in the area.

Bullfrog

In all their life stages, bullfrogs (left) are important in the Gray Lodge food web and are preyed upon by otters, snakes, wading birds, and other wildlife. One day, I caught a western aquatic garter snake in the process of swallowing a bullfrog (right). The frog lucked out and escaped.

Dragonflies are welcome at Gray Lodge. The developing nymphs live in water for several weeks, feeding on mosquito larvae and other water life. Adults are sometimes called mosquito hawks. A band of dragonflies can dramatically reduce the mosquitoes in an area in two or three days. They then move on to another area for another good feed.

A manager tries to be aware of the significant species on the area, their habitat needs, feeding habits, population numbers, and impact on one another and on the area's primary objective. My chief mandate at Gray Lodge was to develop marshland and maintain it to provide sanctuary and food for wintering and resident waterfowl, to provide public hunting and fishing opportunities, and to provide control of illegal and unauthorized use. As long as that mandate was fulfilled, I could make habitat improvements to promote the diversity of wildlife. These efforts did, indeed, attract new species to the area as well as increase population numbers of many resident species.

Gray Lodge Food Web

Among the small creatures on the refuge are (clockwise from top left) dragonflies, or darners, also called mosquito hawks (here in the process of emerging from the nymphal stage); western fence lizards, which are eaten by birds and snakes; red swamp crayfish, which consume tadpoles and small frogs; and gopher snakes, which prey on mice, bird eggs, and nestlings.

CHAPTER 6

Hunting on the Refuge

In the late 1940s, when establishment or enlargement of government-owned wildlife areas was being considered, most of the habitat still available was in private ownership, including private gun clubs. Duck hunters who did not belong to these gun clubs therefore strongly supported creating wildlife areas that would provide for public hunting of waterfowl and pheasants. In turn, the hunters would contribute to the conservation, restoration, and maintenance of the marshlands, which they do today more than any other segment of the population of California.

Waterfowl hunters pay fees for hunting licenses and for state and federal duck stamps, and they pay federal taxes on arms and ammunition under the Pittman-Robertson Federal Aid to State Wildlife Restoration Act. This act alone provides the greater percentage of operational costs of all the state wildlife areas. Hunters additionally give strong financial support to private conservation organizations such as the California Waterfowl Association and Ducks Unlimited.

When Gray Lodge received funds to enlarge the refuge in the 1950s, providing for public hunting was one of the three major mandates. My staff and I were fortunate to benefit from the experiences in other areas of the state as we planned for hunting at Gray Lodge.

Sunrise in the Marsh
Early one clear, calm morning, I accompanied my friend Tom Glaviano to his hunting pond (opposite). It was a wonderful time to be in the marsh and see it come alive with snow geese (above) and other waterfowl. I asked Tom to place his decoys in the water and pose so I could photograph him, along with the surrounding marsh and the hills in the distance, as the sun was about to rise.

Public hunting had been allowed since 1945 on state areas at Honey Lake, Madeline Plains, and Imperial Valley. Then, in 1950, the U.S. Fish and Wildlife Service and the California Department of Fish and Game worked together to develop a program to provide low-cost hunting opportunities for the general public on federal refuges. Under the agreement, the federal staff was responsible for developing and maintaining roads, parking areas, and ponds, and the state staff was responsible for managing hunters and hunting on the given area.

Public hunting in the Sacramento Valley was first permitted on the Colusa National Wildlife Refuge, about twenty-five miles southwest of Gray Lodge. I was assigned to operate the public hunting activities at Colusa with Gray Lodge staff for the first three seasons. We constructed a makeshift check station, hauled it to the site, posted the hunting areas, learned the regulations, and were ready to go on opening day. Hunting was permitted on 1,090 acres of the 4,040-acre refuge.

One-Bird Average Day

On this day in early January of 1972, about one million birds were estimated to be on the sanctuary area of Gray Lodge. A total of 450 hunters were checked in during the day. The surprise was that they averaged only one bird per hunter, for a total of 450 birds. This was not unusual as many variables other than number of birds available have an impact on hunter success. On that day, there was no wind, so the birds did not fly about much. Also, because of the full moon the previous night, the birds had fed all night and did not need to fly off to their feeding grounds until hunting hours had ended.

My staff and I learned the importance of clear maps, instructions, signage, good roads, parking areas, and zoning. Staff was trained to be friendly and helpful and to make sure all regulations and ground rules were clearly understood. We realized that it was important to have visible patrol of the area and to be firm about revoking permits and escorting off those

The First Year

Facilities and operations at Gray Lodge were rather crude in 1953 (top), the first year of public hunting on the area, as we had little preparation time. Hunters checked in at this small shed and then formed a line in their cars and followed the refuge pickup to a hunting area. There were no access roads, and hunters parked along the bordering county roads. Still, for the season, we had 2,113 hunters who shot 8,549 waterfowl. Both Gray Lodge and Sutter refuges averaged four birds per hunter, the highest average of any of the eleven areas then open to hunting. Duck bag limit was seven plus a four-pintail bonus. Two years later, we built a permanent station (above left) where hunters checked in and went to have their hunting take tallied afterward. Species, sex, and age (adult or young of the year) were recorded for all birds bagged.

who did not follow the regulations. I was grateful for the three years spent at the Colusa refuge but was glad to be relieved of that duty in order to open public hunting on Gray Lodge in 1953.

During the 1950s, the development of areas for public hunting of waterfowl in the Central Valley grew rapidly. By 1955, eleven such areas had been opened, including both state-managed federal areas and state areas such as Gray Lodge. Except for the Imperial Waterfowl Management Area in Southern California, all were between the Los Banos Waterfowl Management Area in the San Joaquin Valley and the Madeline Plains Waterfowl Management Area in the north.

Each year, the California Department of Fish and Game determined the number of hunters allowed on each area. The access, or hunter quotas, varied from year to year, depending on the condition of the habitat, and generally was based on the wetland acreage in the hunting area. The ratio was one hunter per ten to fifteen acres of pond. The amount of tule cover also affected the hunter quota, as did the size of available parking areas.

In 1953, Gray Lodge had enough roads, parking areas, and ponds to provide hunting on about twelve hundred acres. Our quota was 80 hunters, the same quota we had managed on Colusa. As we acquired more lands and improved the water delivery system, additional wetlands were developed. Roads and parking areas were increased. By 1960, our quota was up to 160. With the addition of the Brady Ranch in 1970, the quota was raised to 300; after purchase of the Cassady Ranch in 1974, it was increased to 400 hunters, where it has remained. Both of these ranches had previously leased areas for private hunting, which were easily converted for public hunting.

After the first year of operating public hunting on the Colusa refuge, we had divided the hunting area into zones, each with a numbered parking

New Check Station

The high ground at the junction of Pennington Road and the Gray Lodge entrance was chosen for the site of permanent check station facilities (bottom). The station was completed in time for the 1955 season and is still in use. Within five years, the parking area had to be enlarged. When

the hunter capacity went to four hundred in 1974, the parking area was enlarged again. As more hunters came in motor homes and travel trailers in order to stay over between shoot days, an area was established at the west end of the parking area for RVs and tents. Some hunters made a pit for playing horseshoes (left). This also proved to be a popular spot for socializing and spending time between hunts.

A Heavy Load
Hunters sometimes had to hike up to three-quarters of a mile to get from the parking area to their favorite hunting pond while toting a sack of decoys, a shotgun, shells, and extra coats, and wearing heavy rubber boots or waders. At the end of the shoot, they had to add the take of the day to the load. This group of hunters solved the problem with a little red wagon.

lot. As hunters signed in, they were assigned to a specific parking lot and zone. This enabled us to disperse hunters evenly on the area and to prevent them from wandering all over the refuge. In preparing for hunting activities on Gray Lodge, we took a similar approach, locating the roads, ponds, and parking areas so the refuge could be broken into zones. In some of the ponds in the hunting area, we constructed little islands about one hundred yards apart and planted cover for the hunters.

Check station facilities were established on a five-acre parking area at the intersection of Pennington Road and the Gray Lodge headquarters entrance. We used temporary sheds for the first two seasons, then built a permanent building. We also put in a well and tankhouse to provide potable water and toilet facilities. There was some doubt on the part of my supervisors at the California Department of Fish and Game about the need for such extensive facilities, but when we had to accommodate over seventeen thousand hunters a season, the facilities weren't too big at all.

In 1952, the Sacramento Valley Waterfowl Advisory Committee, made up of rice growers and representatives of sportsmen clubs, was formed primarily to make recommendations to the California Department of Fish and Game and the U.S. Fish and Wildlife Service regarding rice crop depredation in the Sacramento Valley. On the advice of this committee, opening day for waterfowl hunting was consistently delayed on state and federal areas in the Sacramento Valley until the estimated end of rice harvest, usually around October 25. The date of opening day is still dependent on the recommendations of this committee, but it is no longer consistently delayed because improvements in rice varieties and harvesting equipment have made possible earlier and shorter harvest periods. Traditional waterfowl shoot days were Saturday, Sunday, and Wednesday, plus Election Day, Veteran's Day, and Thanksgiving. The three-week pheasant hunting season opened the second Saturday in November. Both pheasants and ducks could be hunted on waterfowl shoot days, but only pheasants could be hunted on the other days until the end of the pheasant season. At Gray Lodge,

Junior Pheasant Hunter
This twelve-year-old was proud of bagging his first pheasant. Licensed junior hunters, those under age sixteen, could hunt with a companion over age eighteen. Many father-son partners hunted together during the first week of pheasant season. Even more came when we held special coot shoots during the 1960s. Young hunters had a better chance with the coots than with the wily pheasants.

the busiest hunt day every year was the opening day of pheasant season, when both ducks and pheasants could be hunted. The quota on pheasant-only days was the same, four hundred hunters at a time.

Pheasant hunting was for roosters only. Most seasons, the majority of the kill was taken in the first week. Roosters quickly learned to sit tight or move into heavy cover, or even move off Gray Lodge. This behavior ensured plenty of roosters come spring, and the remaining roosters established territories with harems of hens with the breeding potential to replace the hunting take. After a few years, it was decided that hunter numbers didn't warrant the expense and staff time to keep the area open every day after the first week, but pheasants could still be hunted on traditional duck shoot days.

Ring-necked Pheasants

At the beginning of the season, hunters on Gray Lodge may see male pheasants in full plumage in small groups. However, pheasants quickly learn to be wary. Although some birds sit tight, most scatter, and some even move off the area. Hunter success drops dramatically after the first few days of the pheasant season. Thereafter, only hunters with good dogs have much success.

Waterfowl hunters have had two options for accessing the area: the reservation system and the first-come, first-served system. Applications for reservations were received at Department of Fish and Game in Sacramento prior to the hunting date desired. Hunters whose applications were drawn in the lottery were notified by mail before their hunting date. For Gray Lodge, four hundred reservations were allotted for each hunt day. The first-come, first-served system required hunters to go to the areas where they wished to hunt, register, and park their vehicles in the order in which they arrived.

Never did all the hunters holding reservations show up. The closest we came was one day when all but twelve arrived, but the no-shows were usually around fifty. Once all hunters with reservations had been processed, enough hunters from the

Champion Hunter

We did not keep records on individual hunters, but if we had, I feel sure they would show that Ron Fresvik from Oroville was the most successful Gray Lodge hunter, at least during my tenure. He did not miss many shoot days during the season. It was a rarity for him to check out without a limit of birds. He was a fine dog trainer, with outstanding retrievers.

first-come, first-served line were checked in to meet the quota. All hunters had to turn in their permits and report their daily bag before leaving the area. As hunters checked out, others from the first-come, first-served line could replace them. On any given day, many more than four hundred people hunted on the area. Our record was over eight hundred in 1975. Around seven hundred per shoot day was not unusual.

I observed that hunter success varied for several reasons at Gray Lodge. Saturday and Wednesday were better days than Sunday because Sunday followed a hunt day. The birds had a two-day "rest" before the Saturday and Wednesday shoots, allowing them to settle back into the hunting zone. Hunter success was generally better during the "dark of the moon," because the ducks, which are night feeders, could not find food as readily as during periods with a full moon. Consequently, they tended to become more restless during the day and drift off their loafing areas in the

Hunting Mounds

On one of the large fields of the 1974 Cassady Ranch addition, over twenty hunters' mounds, about three feet high and twenty to twenty-five feet in diameter, were constructed (below). They were irregularly dispersed no less than a hundred yards apart. Vegetation naturally grew on the mounds to provide hunting cover. The mounds allowed hunters and their dogs to stand out of the ice-cold ponds and also helped keep hunters separated. In spring, the mounds provided nesting cover for ducks such as cinnamon teal (left), mallards, and gadwalls.

sanctuary areas. When fog hung over ponds and feeding areas for two or more days, the birds were more active and sometimes flew at lower elevations, enhancing hunter success. Hunting was also better on those areas that were in the established flight patterns to nearby feeding areas. Winds tended to encourage the birds to fly about. The first day of a storm provided good hunting, with lower flight paths, bringing more birds into shotgun range. But, thereafter, the birds would be dispersed for several days, and few would settle on established shooting ponds.

Deer Season

I saw the first deer on Gray Lodge in 1964, and the sighting remains a very special memory. As the years went by, deer in and around the marshes were a welcome sight and a distinct pleasure for year-round visitors. The first deer hunting on Gray Lodge was in 1981, the year after I left. Permits were issued for a bow-and-arrow shoot. For the nine-day September 2000 season, a drawing was held for thirty deer tags, one deer per tag, either sex, shotgun only, no dogs allowed.

Instead of constructing permanent blinds, we added a few plantings but mostly let vegetation develop and provide natural cover. Some tank blinds remained on the former hunting club lands. Hunters occasionally brought portable blinds or created blinds in the natural vegetation. We stressed that all hunters should keep in cover as much as possible and respect the rights of other hunters.

Our experiences at the Colusa National Wildlife Refuge taught us the importance of educating and preparing hunters for accessing a public area. Training sessions were held for Gray Lodge staff prior to the opening of hunting season. As the hunters checked in, they were given a map

Setting Out Decoys (ABOVE)

Most experienced hunters learn to use decoys. This pond was a good choice for placement. It was a permanent pond, not a fall-flooded pond. Good waterfowl food plants, especially pondweed and duckweed, had developed. Ducks have a strong tendency to keep returning to these ponds.

Canvasback and Redhead (LEFT)

Although the canvasback (foreground) and redhead (background) are not common on Gray Lodge, these diving ducks are occasionally found in a hunter's bag. I noted an average of four or five pairs of red-heads nesting on the area each year, but never any canvasbacks.

clearly showing all Gray Lodge hunting zones and parking areas. Printed on the reverse side were the legal hunting regulations, plus area regulations encouraging courtesy and respect for fellow hunters. The packet also included a U.S. Fish and Wildlife Service pocket booklet of the most common waterfowl, illustrating both sitting and flight silhouettes. Posted in the check station area were large signs showing the silhouettes of swans and snow geese. The educational efforts, as well as holding tough initially on enforcement of laws and area regulations, were effective. After the first two or three years, we had few problems. This was also because by then the majority of hunters were repeat visitors. Most hunters new to the area came with a seasoned veteran. My staff and I came to recognize and appreciate the sportsmanship exhibited by the majority of hunters, who sort of shamed the few renegades into good behavior.

THERE WERE MANY INTERESTING PEOPLE who came to hunt. Several times a season, a group of first-generation Russians drove up from San Francisco in four or five cars. They thoroughly enjoyed the area and thought the United States was great. They also brought some very interesting foods, which they always invited me to sample. Some hunters arrived in advance, especially before opening weekend, and slept in their cars in order to hold a place in line. By the 1960s, many had travel trailers or motor homes. San Francisco "Sea Captain Paul" always came in his motor home with wife and dogs whenever he was in port. Hunters with RVs could come ahead and stay between shoot days as long as they remained with their vehicles. Over my years at Gray Lodge, the use of RVs increased, especially among first-come, first-served hunters, who sometimes came days ahead to get in line.

Good Hunting Dog
These hunters and their dog had a successful hunt. I always enjoyed observing a well-trained dog and the special relationships between the hunters and their dogs.

Proud Hunter

Few women hunted on Gray Lodge when I was there. Some who came to the area hunted pheasants, others ducks, and most did so as partners with their husbands. Thelma Childers was an exception. She hunted by herself and was pleased to show her bird.

Good friendships developed among strangers who would thereafter rendezvous at Gray Lodge to hunt together. Gradually, many groups formed, returning year after year, meeting around barbecues after a good hunt day. In the evening, I often circulated among the various gatherings. I developed some very good friendships that continue to this day. The aura of fellowship was heartwarming to me.

About half of the Gray Lodge hunters brought a hunting dog. Well-trained dogs are a big advantage on a public area. They can retrieve waterfowl faster than the hunters can alone, with less disturbance to ponds and to other hunters. Also, fewer birds are lost. Dogs are particularly effective in the hunting of pheasants, which can often outsmart a hunter but rarely a dog. At Gray Lodge, the majority of hunters managed their dogs well, and we had few complaints about dogs either in the check-in area or in the field. To me, it was always inspiring to observe the relationships between hunters and their dogs.

By the time I retired in 1980, we had been through twenty-seven seasons of public hunting and had accommodated more than 240,000 hunters. No major hunting accidents had occurred during that time. In 1954, California was the second state in the nation to start a hunter safety program. After that date, people applying for their first resident hunting license had to go through hunter safety training. In the first thirty years, 1.2 million hunters were trained in the program. The accident rate per 10,000 licensed hunters dropped from 3.10 to 0.75 in that same time period.

By the early 1970s, waterfowl hunting began to decline nationwide. In California, between 1970 and 1980, duck stamp sales dropped from 188,861 to 114,825, with a further drop to 81,146 by 1999. Costs increased on all fronts: hunting licenses, duck stamps, hunting area fees, guns, ammunition, food, lodging, and gasoline. Among other factors in the decline were lack of readily accessible places to hunt, more leisure activity options, strong enforcement of private land trespass laws, changing attitudes about hunting, and fewer new-generation hunters. On Gray Lodge, waterfowl hunters for 1977–78 totaled 16,447. By 1996, hunter numbers dropped to 11,978. There was an upswing to 15,153 for the 1999–2000 season.

Concurrent with and partially contributing to the decline in hunters was a decrease in the numbers of wintering waterfowl. Much has been written about the probable causes for the diminishing numbers. It was evident in all flyways and served as a wake-up call to wildlife professionals, conservation groups, and concerned citizens in both the United States and Canada. The result was great strides in research and conservation techniques, on breeding and wintering grounds, by the U.S. Fish and Wildlife Service, the Canadian Wildlife Service, state and provincial wildlife agencies, and nonprofit organizations such as Ducks Unlimited, the Delta Waterfowl Foundation, and the California Waterfowl Association.

For those hunting waterfowl, Gray Lodge remains one of the best locations available to the general public. It has efficient, friendly staff, and it is a well-developed, easily accessed hunting area—and often harbors the biggest concentration of waterfowl in the Sacramento Valley.

CHAPTER 7

Evening Flights

During the fall and winter months, evening is a thrilling time on Gray Lodge, as some birds are coming in to roost for the night and others are leaving to forage and feed outside the refuge. It is the sheer numbers of wildlife that draw attention.

The blackbirds are first to arrive, in small flocks of about two hundred, usually one flock right after another. In ten to fifteen minutes, the flights are over, and thousands of blackbirds have quickly disappeared into the tules for the night. A truly beautiful, graceful flight is that of the sandhill cranes as they come in just after sunset to their favorite pond on the southwest side of the sanctuary. The pond has a large, open area, four to six inches deep, where the sandhills roost for the night to be safe from predators. The numbers differ from year to year, from two to three hundred birds. Also returning in the evening are some of the geese that have flown out earlier to feed. At the same time, black-crowned night-herons emerge from their daytime roosting hideaways in the tules. As they start hunting the open ponds and flooded rice fields, their loud *quarks* enliven the evening sounds.

The most spectacular, awe-inspiring experience is the evening flight of thousands of waterfowl, sometimes over half a million, seen against a backdrop of clouds reflecting the setting sun. It was

Sunset at Gray Lodge
(OPPOSITE AND ABOVE)

Waterfowl at sunset

Herons and egrets

a great treat for my family when we lived on Gray Lodge. At the sound of liftoff, we gathered on our front yard, as did the resident staff families, to watch. Quite often, we drove to the sanctuary loop to be in the middle of the flights.

The evening waterfowl flights at Gray Lodge are primarily duck flights. Most of the wintering ducks have arrived by late October. By middle to late October, most of the waterfowl food in the area has been well gleaned. Thereafter, the birds must forage throughout the Sacramento

Geese in full moon

Valley until they migrate north again. It is during this period, from late October to late January, that the evening flights occur. Ducks, which are night feeders, leave the area to forage, mostly in harvested rice fields. The flights begin a little after sundown, often just as the last geese have arrived for the night. The entire concentration of ducks doesn't suddenly lift off together. Instead, the flights start with singles, pairs, and small groups of birds. Then, suddenly, thousands of birds are in the air.

The flights out occur every evening but are obscured on rainy or stormy days, and after

Evening flights of waterfowl (above) and sandhill cranes (below)

the sun sets. At these times, the moving birds can be heard but not seen. Those flights that touch one's innermost being occur when the sun's last remaining rays are reflected onto thin cloud formations. The silhouettes of birds in flight against the sunlit clouds make for an unforgettable sight. But the view is not the only thrill. The calls of the birds and the thunder of their wing beats combine with the view to create a truly spiritual experience. Quickly, the flight is all over, fifteen to twenty minutes from start to finish.

Hunting With a Camera

WILDLIFE PHOTOGRAPHY is a great hobby and a rewarding way to learn about nature. It can also be more than a hobby. During my years at Gray Lodge Wildlife Area, I used photographs to enliven the numerous government reports required of a wildlife area manager. I also gave many slide shows to a great variety of audiences. I truly enjoyed sharing nature with so many people.

Whether or not you hunt, wildlife photography gets you outdoors and gives you an opportunity to observe and enjoy nature's creatures. The photographic season lasts all year, and the game is almost unlimited. I have been capturing wildlife on film for over fifty years and find the pursuit just as exciting today as it was when I started. Although I cannot cover every aspect of photography, here are some tips that may help you get started.

Many kinds of cameras will do the job. Photographs taken during my tenure at Gray Lodge were made with a 35mm Topcon body and a variety of lenses. Later, I switched to a 35mm Canon digital camera that never fails to amaze and please me. You can begin with a good 35mm camera, with a built-in light meter, that allows a range of shutter speeds, at least to 1/2,000 of a second. High-quality zoom lenses that go to at least 400mm are excellent for relatively

Racer with fly

close-in wildlife photography as they permit quick framing and focusing. The serious wildlife photographer will find that telephoto lenses in the 300mm to 600mm range will increase the opportunity to capture animals that are more wary. When photographing with a telephoto lens, always use a tripod or other camera brace. In the fog or rain, have a plastic bag to keep your camera dry, but continue shooting because many opportunities for interesting pictures can emerge in inclement weather.

Film choices are almost unlimited, and more and more improvements are being made to film. Professionals at reputable photographic equipment stores can give you good advice on the best film to use for any given light condition. Basic understanding of film speed is essential. Briefly, the higher the speed number, the more sensitive the film and the less natural light is required for proper exposure. On the other hand, lower film speeds result in sharper, less grainy photographs. Always be sure to set your camera light meter to the speed rating and the kind of film in use. Remember to protect your film from the sun as heat can have an adverse effect.

When in the field, wear nondescript clothing. I like my camouflage hunting coat with its many pockets so I can carry film, lenses, and other items. During warm weather, a camouflage angler's vest is useful. To minimize facial glare, a hunter's camouflage hat is ideal. Tripods and other gear are often made of aluminum alloy, which is reflective and can startle wildlife. In most cases, you can cover the reflective areas with black or camouflage tape.

Before you go to an area, read about it so you know what to expect, how to prepare, and what to pursue. For example, if you are going to wintering grounds, find out when the maximum concentration of birds will be present and where they feed or gather to rest. If you are interested in mammals, learn their habits and preferred habitats.

A photo blind can be useful. Set it up several days in advance, if possible, so birds and other wildlife get used to it. One way to determine the best location to take pictures is to study flight patterns or animal tracks in the area. Blinds must be made of canvas or a like material that completely conceals you and your movements. Camouflage netting alone is insufficient but is good to drape over the canvas to help conceal the blind.

American white pelican, breeding adult with centerboard

birds such as herons and egrets, the entire colony is highly vulnerable during nesting season, and intrusion may result in abandonment of all nests. Therefore, do not approach nesting areas closely. Instead, use a telephoto lens and a tripod, which allow you to remain a safe distance away.

When you have time to plan a photographic field trip, one good choice is backroad hunting with a camera. Here are a few tips for successful backroad photography.

- Select backroads with diverse wildlife habitats and minimal traffic. A local district game warden might be able to suggest little-used roads where wildlife can be observed.

- Drive slowly and pull out of traffic lanes before stopping. Turn off your motor to eliminate noise and vibrations. Wild animals are less afraid of your car than of you, so stay inside at first, using the car as a blind. While you are in the car or after you get out, avoid making sudden movements and speak softly.

- Brace your telephoto lens on a steadying device such as a bean bag set on top of the open window of your car.

- Never take chances by approaching bears, moose, or other potentially dangerous wildlife. You can still get some great photographs by remaining in your car.

When you are ready to photograph, keep your camera focused on infinity or prefocused on an area where you expect action. For example, focus on tules in a pond where you anticipate birds to fly over. Check light meter readings for both bright and shaded areas so you can rapidly adjust the exposure as necessary. The way to capture birds in flight is to track them with your camera as you gently squeeze the shutter relcase to take the picture. For this situation, the shutter speed should be at least 1/500 of a second.

If you see a few birds on a pond, do not crowd in and scare them. Be patient—they may serve as decoys to bring in more birds, giving you a great picture. If you spot a desired subject before it sees you, approach it very slowly or just let it come to you. Many animals will ignore a motionless object, even a camouflaged human intruder. When focusing on an animal, try to get its eye in sharp focus and capture the "eye shine" for a more lifelike picture. Framing the picture to eliminate man-made structures also makes a photograph more natural.

As in hunting and wildlife watching, ethics are important. Be sure to get permission from landowners before entering private property, and obey parking and hiking regulations on all parks and wildlife areas. Do not leave an established trail to reach the nests of birds or other wildlife or to disrupt their natural cover. Doing so can lead predators to the nest site. Intruding upon a nest can also cause abandonment, particularly if eggs are in early stages of incubation. With rookery

Wherever you do your photographic wildlife hunting, it will be a rewarding experience. You might want to set goals, such as monthly, seasonal, or yearly wish lists of the species you want to capture on film. A big advantage of becoming a wildlife photographer is that you will gradually become a more knowledgeable naturalist. As you learn more about wildlife and gain photographic experience, your enjoyment of the activity and your skills will increase. Good luck and happy hunting!

Wood Duck Nest Boxes

PEOPLE WHO WANT to increase waterfowl numbers can make a contribution by participating in a wood duck nest box project. One California volunteer who checks and services his 150 boxes throughout the nesting season hatches as many as two thousand ducklings each year. Here are some basic guidelines to consider when building and installing nest boxes, along with plans for constructing a box.

Numerous materials and designs for wood duck nest boxes have been tested. Wood has been proven to be the safest material to use, as it stays cool. Metal and plastic boxes may become hot inside and therefore kill developing embryos. Redwood, western cedar, and rough-cut exterior plywood have all been used successfully by nesting wood ducks. Redwood and cedar are more expensive but are resistant to rotting and therefore are more durable than other woods. Wood boxes should not be painted, as some paints contain toxic chemicals. Also, various colors absorb or reflect light differently and may alter the nest box environment.

When constructing a nest box, keep in mind that the correct size and shape of the entrance hole are extremely important. The hole should be an elliptical opening three inches high and four inches wide, as shown in the illustrations on the opposite page. This size and shape allow sufficient room for female wood ducks to enter a box, but are small enough to deter large predators such as raccoons. Wood ducks may reject boxes that have entrances smaller or much larger than the recommended size.

When plywood or other smooth-surface woods are used, an inside ladder must be provided so that ducklings can get out of the box. This ladder should extend from the nest material inside the box up to the entrance hole. It can be made by taking a sharp object, such as a wood chisel, or a power tool, such as a router, and carving a crosshatch pattern in the wood.

Proper construction of nest boxes is only one aspect of ensuring their use by wood ducks. As wood ducks do not bring nesting material to a cavity, three to four inches of wood shavings must be provided in the bottom of each box. Boxes need to be placed where adequate riparian habitat is available to support wood duck broods from hatching to flight. They can be installed over water or over ground within two hundred feet of a creek, pond, or other waterway. Boxes supported on poles over water should be at least three feet above the highest water level anticipated during nesting. Boxes over dry ground should be installed eight to twelve feet high to discourage predators. Predator guards, in the form of sheet metal cones, can be used on trees or poles.

Once you have built a nest box to the correct specifications shown here and have installed it properly, routine maintenance is the key to a successful project. Boxes need to be visited at least four times during the nesting season so that data collecting, necessary repairs, and other tasks such as replenishing nesting material can be accomplished.

Before you decide to build a nest box for wood ducks, you'll want to read in greater detail about locating and installing a box and about the required maintenance. *A Guide to Installing and Managing Wood Duck Boxes*, available for a nominal cost from the California Waterfowl Association (see address on page 4), includes maintenance schedules, supply lists for pre-, mid-, and postseason checks, and color photographs of boxes in use. Supplies and preconstructed nest boxes can be purchased through CWA. If you live outside California, contact your state's waterfowl association, wildlife agency, or local chapter of Ducks Unlimited for further information.

Plans for Making a Wood Duck Nest Box

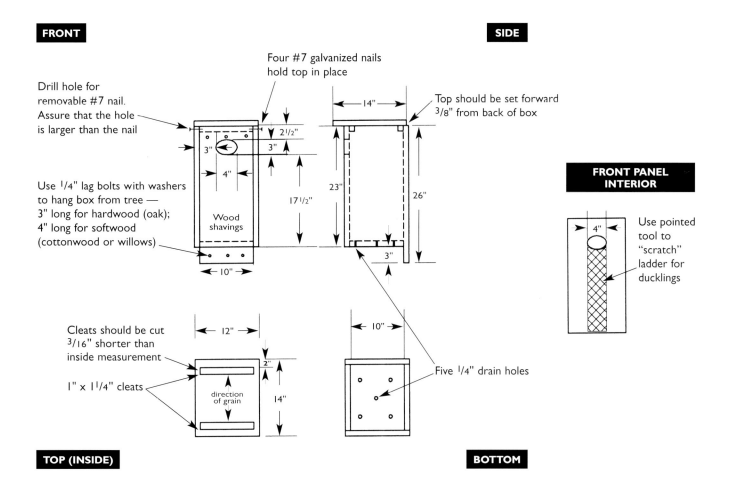

FRONT

Drill hole for removable #7 nail. Assure that the hole is larger than the nail

Use 1/4" lag bolts with washers to hang box from tree — 3" long for hardwood (oak); 4" long for softwood (cottonwood or willows)

Four #7 galvanized nails hold top in place

Wood shavings

2 1/2"
3"
4"
17 1/2"
3"
10"

SIDE

Top should be set forward 3/8" from back of box

14"
23"
26"
3"

FRONT PANEL INTERIOR

Use pointed tool to "scratch" ladder for ducklings

4"

TOP (INSIDE)

Cleats should be cut 3/16" shorter than inside measurement

1" x 1 1/4" cleats

12"
2"
14"
direction of grain

BOTTOM

Five 1/4" drain holes

10"

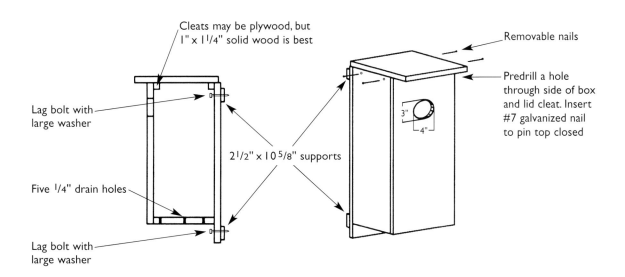

Cleats may be plywood, but 1" x 1 1/4" solid wood is best

Lag bolt with large washer

Five 1/4" drain holes

Lag bolt with large washer

2 1/2" x 10 5/8" supports

Removable nails

Predrill a hole through side of box and lid cleat. Insert #7 galvanized nail to pin top closed

3"
4"

Appendix III

Mourning Dove Wire Cone Nests

WIRE NESTS have proven to be beneficial aids to mourning doves. They are easy to fabricate and install. Use the following instructions to make and install a cone nest.

For optimal use, nests should be placed in or near established nesting areas. If a nest is destroyed, doves are unlikely to move their nest more than thirty yards. The best sites are along tree limbs with forked branches and moderate shade. Doves are not fussy in their choice of trees used for nesting, but the birds need good visibility from the nest and the ability to escape easily

in several directions. Therefore, don't select sites with heavy, brushy growth. Also remember that doves will not search farther than sixty feet from their nest location to find nesting materials. At Gray Lodge Wildlife Area, I found that doves preferred nests six to eight feet above ground.

The wire cone nests can be put up at any time of the year, but for best results, cones should be installed by the end of March, making them available to early mature nesters, first-time nesters, and migrants that nest by June.

1. Purchase ¼-inch or ⅜-inch galvanized wire mesh hardware cloth, sold in most hardware stores. Using tin snips or good wire cutters, cut a 12-inch square for each nest.

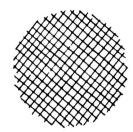

2. Cut off the 4 corners of the square to make a rough circle.

3. Cut a 4-inch wedge from the circle, as you would cut a piece of pie. The nests can be left flat for transporting or storage.

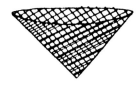

4. Just prior to installation, close the pie cut by overlapping the edges about 3 inches to make a cone.

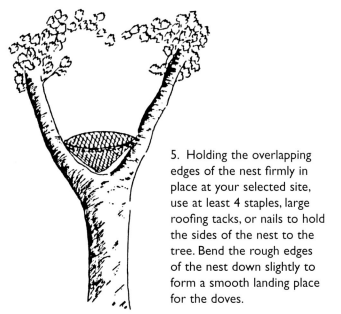

5. Holding the overlapping edges of the nest firmly in place at your selected site, use at least 4 staples, large roofing tacks, or nails to hold the sides of the nest to the tree. Bend the rough edges of the nest down slightly to form a smooth landing place for the doves.

Mammals, Reptiles, and Amphibians of Gray Lodge Wildlife Area

FROM 1947 TO 1979, the Gray Lodge staff and I kept notes about our observations of mammals, reptiles, and amphibians. In 1979, I compiled a booklet describing the species found on the area, illustrated with sketches by Bob Hines. It was published in 1979 by the California Department of Fish and Game. The following updated list is from that publication.

Mammals
Opossum
Adorned shrew
Vagrant shrew
Broad-handed mole
Big brown bat
Brazilian free-tailed bat
California myotis
Hoary bat
Pallid bat
Red bat
Raccoon
Ringtail

Mink
River otter
Spotted skunk
Striped skunk
Badger
Red fox
Gray fox
Coyote
Feral house cat
Muskrat
Beaver
Beechey ground squirrel
Valley pocket gopher

Western harvest mouse
Deer mouse
California vole
Feral house mouse
Norway rat
Black rat
Black-tailed jackrabbit
Desert cottontail
Black-tailed deer

Reptiles
Western pond turtle
Western fence lizard

Southern alligator lizard
Racer
Gopher snake
Western aquatic
 garter snake
Common garter snake
Western terrestrial
 garter snake
Common king snake

Amphibians
Pacific treefrog
Bullfrog

Striped skunks

Birds of the Gray Lodge and Upper Butte Basin Wildlife Areas

THE FOLLOWING BIRDS have been observed at Gray Lodge and at Upper Butte Basin to the north. Some species are resident and nest on these areas; others, such as many waterfowl, are present only part of the year. Still others are rare and not seen every year. A published version of the list includes information on seasonality of species and a map of federal and state refuges in Northern California. Distributed by the California Department of Fish and Game and sponsored by the California Waterfowl Association, the list is given to Gray Lodge visitors.

Grebes
Eared grebe
Horned grebe
Pied-billed grebe
Western grebe

Pelicans and Cormorants
American white pelican
Double-crested
    cormorant

Bitterns, Herons, and Egrets
American bittern
Least bittern
Great blue heron
Cattle egret
Great egret
Snowy egret
Black-crowned
    night-heron
Green heron

Ibises
White-faced ibis

Waterfowl
Bufflehead
Canvasback
Ring-necked duck
Ruddy duck
Wood duck
Gadwall
Common goldeneye
Canada goose

Greater white-fronted
    goose
Ross's goose
Snow goose
Mallard
Hooded merganser
Common merganser
Northern pintail
Redhead
Greater scaup
Lesser scaup
Northern shoveler
Tundra swan
Blue-winged teal
Cinnamon teal
Green-winged teal
American wigeon
Eurasian wigeon

Vultures, Eagles, Hawks, and Falcons
Bald eagle
Golden eagle
Peregrine falcon
Prairie falcon
Northern harrier
Cooper's hawk
Ferruginous hawk
Red-tailed hawk
Red-shouldered hawk
Rough-legged hawk
Sharp-shinned hawk
Swainson's hawk
American kestrel
White-tailed kite

Merlin
Osprey
Turkey vulture

Gallinaceous Birds
Ring-necked pheasant
California quail

Rails
American coot
Common moorhen
Virginia rail
Sora

Cuckoos
Yellow-billed cuckoo

Pigeons and Doves
Rock dove
Mourning dove
Band-tailed pigeon

Shorebirds, Snipe, and Phalaropes
American avocet
Long-billed curlew
Long-billed dowitcher
Dunlin
Killdeer
Red-necked phalarope
Wilson's phalarope
Black-bellied plover
Semipalmated plover
Baird's sandpiper
Least sandpiper

Pectoral sandpiper
Solitary sandpiper
Spotted sandpiper
Western sandpiper
Common snipe
Black-necked stilt
Willet
Whimbrel
Greater yellowlegs
Lesser yellowlegs

Gulls and Terns
California gull
Herring gull
Ring-billed gull
Black tern
Caspian tern
Forster's tern

Cranes
Greater sandhill crane
Lesser sandhill crane

Owls
Burrowing owl
Barn owl
Great horned owl
Long-eared owl
Short-eared owl
Western screech owl

Goatsuckers
Lesser nighthawk
Common poorwill

Swifts
Vaux's swift
White-throated swift

Hummingbirds
Anna's hummingbird
Black-chinned
   hummingbird
Rufous hummingbird

Kingfishers
Belted kingfisher

Woodpeckers
Northern flicker
Red-breasted sapsucker
Acorn woodpecker
Downy woodpecker
Lewis's woodpecker
Nuttall's woodpecker

Flycatchers
Ash-throated flycatcher
Dusky flycatcher
Gray flycatcher
Olive-sided flycatcher
Western flycatcher
Willow flycatcher
Western kingbird
Western wood-pewee
Black phoebe
Say's phoebe

Swallows
Purple martin
Bank swallow
Barn swallow
Cliff swallow
Northern rough-winged
   swallow
Tree swallow
Violet-green swallow

**Jays, Magpies, Crows,
and Ravens**
American crow
Western scrub jay
Yellow-billed magpie
Common raven

Titmice and Bushtits
Bushtit
Oak titmouse

Nuthatches and Creepers
Brown creeper
Red-breasted nuthatch
White-breasted nuthatch

Wrens
Bewick's wren
House wren
Marsh wren

**Kinglets and
Gnatcatchers**
Blue-gray gnatcatcher
Golden-crowned kinglet
Ruby-crowned kinglet

Thrushes
Western bluebird
American robin
Hermit thrush
Swainson's thrush
Varied thrush

**Mockingbirds
and Thrashers**
Northern mockingbird

Larks and Pipits
American pipit
Horned lark

Waxwings
Cedar waxwing

Shrikes
Loggerhead shrike
Northern shrike

Starlings
European starling

Vireos
Cassin's vireo
Warbling vireo

Weavers
House sparrow

Warblers
Yellow-breasted chat
Black-throated gray
   warbler
Hermit warbler
MacGillivray's warbler
Nashville warbler
Orange-crowned warbler
Townsend's warbler
Wilson's warbler
Yellow warbler
Yellow-rumped warbler
Common yellowthroat

**Tanagers, Grosbeaks,
and Buntings**
Lazuli bunting
Black-headed grosbeak
Blue grosbeak
Western tanager

Towhees and Sparrows
Dark-eyed junco
Chipping sparrow
Fox sparrow
Golden-crowned sparrow
Harris's sparrow
Lark sparrow
Lincoln's sparrow
Savannah sparrow
Song sparrow
Vesper sparrow
White-crowned sparrow
White-throated sparrow
California towhee
Spotted towhee

Blackbirds and Orioles
Brewer's blackbird
Red-winged blackbird
Tricolored blackbird
Yellow-headed blackbird
Brown-headed cowbird
Western meadowlark
Hooded oriole
Bullock's oriole

Finches
House finch
Purple finch
American goldfinch
Lesser goldfinch
Evening grosbeak
Pine siskin

*The following
additional birds
are of accidental
occurrence:*

Little blue heron
Fulvous whistling duck
Baikal teal
Long-tailed duck
White-winged scoter
Red-breasted merganser
Northern goshawk
Yellow rail
Black rail
Snowy plover
Marbled godwit
Ruddy turnstone
Franklin's gull
Bonaparte's gull
Thayer's gull
Glaucous-winged gull
Hairy woodpecker
Mountain bluebird
Sage thrasher
Phainopepla
Northern parula
Magnolia warbler
Palm warbler
Northern waterthrush
Green-tailed towhee
Rufous-crowned sparrow
American tree sparrow
Sage sparrow
Vermilion flycatcher
Great-tailed grackle
European jacksnipe
American black duck

Bibliography

Bailey, James A., William Elder, and Ted D. McKinney, eds. *Readings in Wildlife Conservation.* Wildlife Society, 1974.

Bellrose, Frank C. *Ducks, Geese and Swans of North America.* Stackpole, 1976.

Bidwell, John. *Echoes of the Past, The Century Illustrated Monthly Magazine,* 1890. Reproduced by California Department of Parks and Recreation, 1974.

California Waterfowl Association. *California Mallard Program, 1998 Annual Report.*

———. *California Wood Duck Program, Final Report, 1998.*

———. *A Guide to Installing and Managing Wood Duck Boxes.* 1994.

Carper, H. D. *A Plan for Protecting, Enhancing, and Increasing California's Wetlands for Waterfowl.* California Department of Fish and Game, 1983.

Cowan, John B. "The Evolution of a Refuge into a Wildlife Area." *Outdoor California,* January-February 1999.

———. "The Fascination of Migration." *Outdoor California,* May-June 1974.

———. "Gray Lodge." *Outdoor California,* June 1964.

———. "Hunting on the Public Areas." *Outdoor California,* January-February 1976. Revised and republished, September-October 1986.

———. "The Life History of a Population of Western Mourning Dove." *California Fish and Game Quarterly,* October 1952.

———. "Market Hunting, Part I: Outlaw Hunters Waged War on Ducks." *Outdoor California,* January-February 1992.

———. "Market Hunting, Part II: The War on Outlaws; Federal War on Market Hunters." *Outdoor California,* March-April 1992.

———. "Marshland Cafeteria." *Outdoor California,* September-October 1972.

———. "Marshlands Are for the Birds." *Outdoor California,* May-June 1970.

———. "Nests of Wire Help Doves Improve on Nature." *Outdoor California,* July 1957.

———. "Pre-Fab Wire Mesh Cones Give Doves Better Nest Than They Can Build Themselves." *Outdoor California,* January 1959.

———. "Waterfowl History in the Sacramento Valley." *Outdoor California,* January-February 1985.

———. "Wildlife Management and Mosquito Suppression from the Waterfowl Manager's View." Coordinated Program on Wildlife Management and Mosquito Suppression, conference proceedings, 1962.

———. "Wildlife Values." *Outdoor California,* January-February 1986.

Cowan, John B., with J. H. Ives. "A High Pheasant Nest Density on the Gray Lodge Waterfowl Management Area." *California Fish and Game Quarterly,* October 1966.

Dasmann, Raymond F. *The Destruction of California.* Macmillan, 1965.

Dillon, Richard. *Siskiyou Trail: The Hudson's Bay Company Route to California.* McGraw-Hill, 1975.

Ehrlich, Paul R., David S. Dobkin, and Darryl Wheye. *Birds in Jeopardy.* Stanford University Press, 1992.

Fletcher, Rich. *Hunting Ducks and Geese.* Towhee Publishing, 1987.

Grinnell, Joseph, Joseph Dixon, and Jean Linsdale. *Fur-Bearing Mammals of California.* University of California Press, 1937.

Hawkins, A. S., R. C. Hanson, H. K. Nelson, and H. M. Reeves. *Flyways.* U.S. Fish and Wildlife Service, 1984.

Hill, Dorothy. *The Indians of Chico Rancheria.* California Department of Parks and Recreation, 1978.

Hockbaum, H. Albert. *Travels and Traditions of Waterfowl.* University of Minnesota Press, 1955.

Ingles, Lloyd G. *Mammals of California and Its Coastal Waters.* Stanford University Press, 1954.

Jamison, E. W., Jr., and Hans J. Peeters. *California Mammals.* University of California Press, 1988.

Johnsgard, Paul A. *Waterfowl of North America.* Indiana University Press, 1975.

Kortright, Francis H. *The Ducks, Geese and Swans of North America.* American Wildlife Institute, 1943.

Kozlik, Frank M. "Waterfowl Hunting Areas Operated by the California Department of Fish and Game." *California Fish and Game Quarterly,* January 1955.

Kroeber, A. L. *Handbook of the Indians of California.* Bulletin 78, Bureau of American Ethnology, Smithsonian Institute, 1925; reprinted by California Book Co., 1967.

Lechleitner, Robert. *The Black-tailed Jack Rabbit on Gray Lodge Waterfowl Area, California.* Ph.D. dissertation, University of California, Berkeley, 1955.

Leopold, Aldo. "The Conservation Ethic." *Journal of Forestry,* University of Wisconsin, October 1933.

———. *Game Management.* Scribners, 1933.

Leopold, A. Starker. *The California Quail.* University of California Press, 1977.

Linduska, Joseph P., ed. *Waterfowl Tomorrow.* U.S. Bureau of Fisheries and Wildlife, 1964.

Maloney, A. B. *John Work, 1832–1833: Fur Brigade to the Bonaventura.* California Historical Society, 1945.

Mayer, Kenneth E., and William F. Laudenslayer, Jr., eds. *A Guide to Wildlife Habitats of California.* California Department of Forestry and Fire Protection, 1988.

McGowan, Joseph A. *History of the Sacramento Valley, Volume I.* Lewis Historical Publishing, 1961.

McLandress, M. Robert. *Status of Ross' Geese in California,* Reprint from *Management and Biology of Pacific Flyway Geese: A Symposium.* OSU Book Stores, Inc., 1979.

McLandress, M. Robert, Gregory S. Yarris, Alison E. H. Perkins, Daniel P. Connelly, and Dennis G. Raveling. "Nesting Biology of Mallards in California." *Journal of Wildlife Management,* January 1996.

Morgan, Dale L. *Jedediah Smith and the Opening of the West.* University of Nebraska, 1953.

Nelson, Lewis, Jr., and Jon K. Hooper. *Principles of Wildlife Management.* University of California, Davis, 1974.

Peterson, Roger Tory. *A Field Guide to Western Birds.* Houghton Mifflin, 1961.

Robbins, W. W., Margaret K. Bellue, and Walter S. Ball. *Weeds of California.* California Department of Agriculture, 1970.

Rogers, Justus H. *Colusa County: Its History Traced From a State of Nature Through the Early Period of Settlement and Development to the Present Day.* Colusa County Historical Society, 1891.

Sacramento Valley Waterfowl Habitat Management Committee, John B. Cowan, chair. *Pacific Flyway Waterfowl in California's Sacramento Valley Wetlands.* 1983.

Schemnitz, Sanford, ed. *Wildlife Management Techniques Manual.* Wildlife Society, 1980.

Smith, Jedediah Strong. *The Southwest Expedition of Jedediah Smith: His Personal Account of the Journey to California, 1826–1827.* University of Nebraska, 1977.

Smith, Michael Frances. *Small Mammal Populations Associated with Certain Plant Communities in Gray Lodge Wildlife Area.* Master's thesis, Chico State University, 1975.

Stebbins, Robert C. *A Field Guide to Western Reptiles and Amphibians.* Houghton Mifflin, 1966.

Stefferud, Alfred, ed. *Birds in Our Lives.* U.S. Fish and Wildlife Service, 1966.

Sullivan, Maurice S. *Jedediah Smith, Trader and Trail Breaker.* Press of the Pioneers, 1936.

Trost, Robert, comp. *1998 Pacific Flyway Data Book*, U.S. Fish and Wildlife Service, Office of Migratory Bird Management, 1998.

———. *Pacific Flyway, 1998–99 Fall and Winter Survey Report*, U.S. Fish and Wildlife Service, Office of Migratory Bird Management, 1999.

Wilson, Joseph P., ed. *Rice in California.* Butte County Rice Growers Association, 1979.

Worcester, Hugh M. *Hunting the Lawless.* American Wildlife Associates, 1955.

Yarris, Gregory S., M. Robert McLandress, and Alison E. H. Perkins. "Molt Migration of Postbreeding Female Mallards from Suisun Marsh, California." *The Condor*, 1994.

Zeiner, David C., William. F. Laudenslayer, Jr., Kenneth E. Mayer, and Marshall White. *California's Wildlife, Vol. I, Amphibians and Reptiles.* California Department of Fish and Game, 1988.

———. *California's Wildlife, Vol. II, Birds.* California Department of Fish and Game, 1990.

———. *California's Wildlife, Vol. III, Mammals.* California Department of Fish and Game, 1990.

Index

*Page numbers in italics
refer to photographs or maps.*

Acknowledgments

I am truly grateful to the people who helped make this book a reality and want to thank the following:

Henry Trione, longtime friend, for his continuous encouragement to write the book and for his financial and moral support. Thanks also for being a good neighbor to Gray Lodge for thirty-six years as owner-manager of the adjoining Tule Goose Club, and for giving financial support to student research projects on Gray Lodge in coordination with Dr. A. Starker Leopold and the University of California, Berkeley.

Avis Cowan, my wife and partner since June 3, 1945. Her invaluable support, research, organization, and computer time have been far beyond the call of duty.

California Waterfowl Association, especially to Dr. M. Robert McLandress, President, and Becky Easter, Director of Communications, for their interest and direction, and also to Greg Yarris, Director of Waterfowl Programs, and Dan Loughman, Senior Biologist, for their assistance.

Judith Dunham, managing editor, for skillfully and gracefully guiding the project from the beginning and for her unfailing encouragement and assistance at every stage.

Lory Poulson and Susan Gluck, of Poulson Gluck Design, for giving my words and photographs such an elegant and thoughtful presentation.

Elaine Prater, family friend, sounding board, and supporter, who did typing and organization of the early draft.

Current Gray Lodge staff, Mike Womack, Manager, and Charlotte Lockhart, Administrative Secretary.

The following people, a wide range of professionals, specialists, co-workers, and friends listed in alphabetical order, contributed in various ways to my professional growth, knowledge, and enjoyment in my efforts to help wildlife through the years.

Bill Burleson, Ray Burmaster, Kathy Russell Campbell, Lawrence Cloyd, Ed Collins, Bruce Conant, Debi Conway, Joshua Cowan, Darold Daly, Bruce Deuel, Dave Dick, Al Farres, Bill Fischer, Doug Flesher, Rich Fletcher, John Flores, Monte Ford, Rusty Ford, Myron Fountain, Sam Gridley, Jr., Chet Hart, Bob Hines, Terry Hodges, Steve Hrinsin, Gary Kerhoulas, Jim King, Taber Kopan, Frank Kozlik, Gary Kramer, Bob LaDonne, Howard Leach, Cal Lensink, Fred Lesan, Frank McBride, Diane McCracken, Larry McKibben, Mike Miller, Leo Nomellini, Glenn Olson, Bob Orange, Lee Otterson, Debbie Peterson, Chet Ramsey, Bud Reinecker, Alexia Retallack, E. P. Reynolds, August Sebastiani, Bill Sweeney, Howard Twinning, Jake Walgenbach, Jim Wilson, Roy Wright, Trevor Wright, Dave Zeiner, and last, but not least, the California Department of Fish and Game and the U.S. Fish and Wildlife Service, two remarkably fine government agencies.